The

LifeChange Cookbook

Low-Carbohydrate Essentials for Conquering Fungal Infection

by

Beverly Thornhill Hunt
Ph.D

and

Virginia Hunt O'Brien
OTR, CHT

D1064019

Thornhill Hunt Publications
Dallas, Texas

Published by Thornhill Hunt Publications
P. O. Box 223824
Dallas, TX 75222-3824

Thornhill Hunt Publications Group
Christine Hunt - Graphic Editor
Karen O'Brien - Graphic Artist

**All material is for informational purposes only.
All information contained herein does not take the
place of advice from your physician,
dietitian, or nutritionist.**

From Back Cover: Bunting quote from ~

*Groves, B. PhD. William Bunting: The Father of the
Low-Carbohydrate Diet.* published in Wise Traditions in
Food, Farming and the Healing Arts.
Weston A. Price Foundation. Winter 2002.*

** winner of the Sophie Coe Prize
for the 2002 Oxford Symposium on Food History*

Dedication

Dedicated to Doug Kaufmann...
...who invited me to research the connection
between fungus and cancer. The startling information
I uncovered pointed to a fungal connection not only to
cancer but also to a host of other diseases. Interest in
and response to these findings generated a great need
for a cookbook and for instruction in maintaining
an antifungal lifestyle. My work with Doug began my
endeavors in publishing.

Thank you, Doug.

Beverly

Acknowledgements

All of us are deeply indebted to the work done by many men and women across a number of scientific fields: mycology, food sciences, agricultural sciences, veterinary sciences, biology, and genetics, to name a few. Work done by these dedicated, scientifically-trained individuals undergirds our work today as we piece together the puzzle of fungal involvement in human health.

Beverly

I agreed to work with my mother, Beverly Hunt, in writing this cookbook because I knew it would be a great addition to all she has taught me about health and cooking. Little did I know what a great project it would be! Thank you, Mom, for asking me to be a part of this.

Moms are, from birth, our primary source of nourishment. I remember the first author my parents avidly followed when I was a child: Adele Davis, her book *Let's Eat Right to Keep Fit*, and the "new thought" on nutrition ~ less sugar and more vitamin C, oranges, brewer's yeast, wheat germ, and bran. Mom was always a voracious learner and loved to share her knowledge. This has been true in her quest for the truth regarding fungus and its link to disease.

My mom has continued to be my inspiration and teacher even as I have reached middle age. Since she cares deeply for her children, I have been on the listening end of "today's new understandings;" and with great dividends. Without her recent discoveries, I can truly say I would not be as healthy as I am now and would not have the resources to seek out answers for my own questions. I successfully follow the concepts of the *LifeChange Living* diet and use natural antifungals to fight what ails me and my family of five. Even my college-age children know how to keep themselves healthier in the midst of their roommates, friends, and busy lives.

Because of both the environment and the society in which we live, it is difficult to achieve a state of good health. It is also very difficult to go against the "accepted" understanding of medical health. With the support of the body of knowledge my mother has acquired for healthy living, I feel certain that this cookbook will both bless you and your family and will give you the knowledge you need to seek answers for yourself in your quest for good health.

Many thanks also to my sister-in-law, Christine Hunt, for her exceptional knowledge of the English language, syntax, and visual form of the typed word. She also has been a great partner in testing, creating, altering, and proofreading recipes. We could not have done it without you. Thanks so much.

Virginia

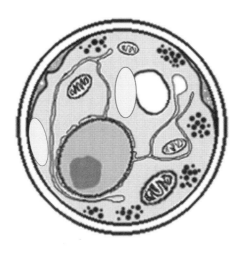

Diagram of a cross section of a
generalized fungal cell

The fungal cell causes much infection because it can infect every system in the body except the teeth.[1] Poor health is expressed in many diseases whose causes are fungi and their mycotoxins. An antifungal diet, as expressed in this cookbook, is one part of the battle for the good health which results from a strong immune system.

1. Male, O. The significance of mycology in medicine. *in* Hawksworth, D. L., ed. Frontiers in mycology. 1991. C A B International. Wallingford, UK.

Font Guide

Words in	Generally indicate
Times New Roman italics	words to be found in the *Appendix: Terms and Glossary*

Table of Contents

x

Introduction

- Enjoying the Return to Good Health -

It is daunting to think of food preparation without the use of common foods such as sugar, flour, potatoes, and milk. The dietary approach offered in *The LifeChange Cookbook* is a departure from the average American's relationship to food. You may find yourself staring transfixed as you read through the listing of allowed and disallowed foods, unable to fathom how to even begin.

This switch to healthier eating habits will take determination and a shift away from the items found in the typical Western cupboard or refrigerator. Take heart! There are ways to include foods that will fit into all the little niches left by the disallowed foods. It will take time, but the absence of overpowering cravings for sweets, potatoes, and breads will feel wonderful.

First, there must come the decision that this LifeChanging lifestyle is important. This change-in-eating lifestyle has three basic purposes:

1. to self-diagnose the possibility of fungal overgrowth,
2. to aid in curing fungal overgrowth, and
3. to build the foundation for recovery from serious ailments ... including cancer.

A significant portion of "what ails us" as human beings is either autoimmune or microbial: bacterial, *viral*, or fungal infection. Also note that viruses are minute fungi.[1]

---

1. Mori, N. *Virus filtrabili e cancro secondo la mia potesi (1914) della loro natura micetica.* 1950. 6. 3-31. Progresso Medico. *in* Livingston-Wheeler, V., Wheeler, O. W. The microbiology of cancer: compendium. 1977. 307-308. Craftsman Graphics. USA.

Research across multiple scientific fields has built a conviction that many autoimmune diseases have microbial causes and are not the result of genetic aberrations. This is pointed out by Milton W. White, a respected medical doctor, surgeon, and medical school instructor, in his definition of cancer. Dr. White spent 50 years researching and publishing on cancer and its cause. His findings were that "Cancer is a chronic, infectious, abnormal, anaerobic, inflammatory, respiratory, and metabolic 'germ' disease."[2]

Though fungi are everywhere, when you are in good health your body balances fungal encounters via your *immune system*. However, an overwhelming exposure to pathogenic fungi, a weakened *immune system*, or dormant fungal spores triggered to grow (the least understood of the fungal processes) can set up an individual for a fungal infection.

Antifungal warfare has three battle fronts for bodily health:

1. medicine ~ whether allopathic, alternative, or a combination,
2. exercise, and
3. diet.

The only one of these that can possibly stand alone is diet. Medicine and/or exercise rarely succeed without a proper antifungal diet. When fungi cause poor health, these powerful organisms can outgrow the benefits of medicine and exercise. An antifungal diet encourages the vitality of the *immune system* by starving the fungi.

Fungi feed on sugars and carbohydrates. Eliminating "fungal feeders" calls for change. We are surrounded by fungal food enticements: ice cream, French fries, candy, alcohol, breads, etc., etc.

There are numerous "anticancerous minor constituents" in foods, including *phytochemicals* (plant chemicals) and colors which

2. White, Milton W. Cancer: the role of oxygen in fungal induced carcinogenesis. 2000. 55(4). 302-05. Medical Hypotheses.

give foods their immune-building and antimicrobial properties. The three major constituents of foods are

> fat, carbohydrates, and protein. Minor constituents have been researched and reported on from scientific studies to newspaper and magazine articles since the mid-20th century. Identification of anticancerous phytochemicals, [i.e.], plant chemicals, were pioneered by Lee W. Wattenberg of the University of Minnesota. He identified many of these agents in laboratory studies.[3]

Dr. Wattenberg's laboratory studies inevitably end with the statement that the mechanism for the food constituents' benefit is "unknown." If cancer, autoimmune diseases, and other conditions are caused by fungus, we *may* know something about the "mechanism." We will discuss some aspects of this theory in the following pages.

This groundbreaking viewpoint on the effect of fungi on human health grew during the years spent editing *The Fungus Link* and doing extensive research for *The Germ That Causes Cancer*. With this shift in the understanding of cause, the fight took a new direction. Individuals can take more responsibility with a careful personal diet and inclusion of available powerful nutrition. Even dreaded cancer can be positively influenced by personal choices of foods containing beneficial nutrition.

Although this is not a weight reduction diet, correctly followed your weight should normalize. It is not uncommon, though, for the body to have a reaction to this diet. If the fungal overgrowth is *mild*, this diet may quickly result in increased well-being, energy, and mental clarity. With a *more serious* overgrowth, the diet may initiate what is known as a Herxheimer's reaction ~ a worsening of one's symptoms as the body sheds the dead fungi and their mycotoxins. This reaction is named for Karl Herxheimer, a 19th century German dermatologist, who described the ill feelings that one can get when

---

3. Greenswald, P. Chemoprevention of Cancer. 275(3). 96-100. Sept 1996. Scientific American.

fungi or other parasites are killed in the body. The reaction is temporary and afterward leads to increased well being. It is difficult to list all the symptoms this reaction may cause since fungi can infect all bodily systems.[4] Among the many reactions, symptoms may include skin irritations, depression, general malaise, headaches, or increased fatigue.

80   CR

It is our hope *The LifeChange Cookbook* will be a useful tool to help you have a positive experience with food in your fight for health. Recipes were compiled from personal sources as well as adapted to fit the antifungal diet and lifestyle. Bear in mind that measurements, techniques, and cooking times may need to be adjusted when you try these recipes in your own kitchen.

Since recipe development is always a work in progress, we hope that you who are in the fight will give us your feedback. Your input and experience are important in the over-all validity of conquering fungal infection.

We also hope these recipes will encourage you in your fight against diet boredom. Step up to the challenge of health-restoring meals: adapt your own recipes, find interesting new tricks in food preparation, and enjoy a healthy *LifeChange*!

Beverly Thornhill Hunt
&
Virginia Hunt O'Brien

4. Male, O. The significance of mycology in medicine. *in* Hawksworth, D. L. Frontiers in mycology. 1991. 131-156. CAB International. Wallingford, UK.

Chapter One

"Tying on a New Apron"

A return to good health requires a three-pronged attack: diet, medication, and exercise. Our goal is to help you in your battle for good health by making it easier for you to use an antifungal diet to prepare delicious, health-restoring meals. It is important to find and correctly use foods which will aid in your return to good health: to know which foods must be strictly avoided, which can be used in moderation, and which can be used freely.

The word is out: fear of fat may be unfounded. Diet-promoters have had to admit that Dr. Atkins may have been right in his long-published low carbohydrate weight-loss diet. Reasons reported in the media are based on epidemiology, that is, surveys and polls which showed people on *low-carbohydrate* diets indeed lost weight.

We agree with the importance of a diet that lowers carbo-hydrates, such as the basis of Dr. Atkins' weight reduction diet, however, our purpose is health restoration not necessarily weight loss. We propose that proliferation of fungi can have a negative effect on human health. *Carbohydrates* in the diet equate to glucose in the body. *Glucose* is the fuel for life, energy, and growth for living organisms, including man and fungi. Fungi overwhelmingly prefer carbohydrates[1]; humans can live well without *carbohydrates*. This makes an antifungal diet possible.

It is impossible to avoid ingesting some fungi. *Antibiotics* are produced by fungi in their ongoing warfare against bacteria.

---

1. Moore-Landecker, E. Fundamentals of the fungi. 4th ed. 1996. Prentice-Hall. Upper Saddle River, NJ.

While antibiotics (made from fungal poisons) have been a boon in eradicating human bacterial enemies, they come with an unwanted negative effect. *Antibiotics* prescribed for illness also eradicate the beneficial bacteria which are an integral part of the human immune system. This compromise of the human immune system is reflected in a dramatic rise in the frequency, proliferation, and distribution of fungal infections during the last 50 years.[2] Since the introduction of antibiotics, the number of identified autoimmune diseases has mushroomed from less than ten in the 1950s to nearly 100 by the end of the 20th century.

Learning a New Way to Think about Food

We have been told to cut the fat out of our diets ~ and that sales pitch has been quite successful. The consumption of fats has declined ~ but the incidence of obesity has increased. We eat less fats and yet we are fatter than ever. Could there be more involved than is being recognized?

Conventional meat products are a significant source of non-prescribed antibiotics (those fungal poisons mentioned above). In the United States, 50 percent of the antibiotics produced are used in animal feeds.[3] Antibiotics and hormones are used to hasten animal maturity and increase the marketable size of animals sold for meat. Antibiotics, hormones, and mycotoxins (the poisonous byproducts of fungi) tend to lodge in the fat of animals and animal products, such as dairy products. Consumption of these products leads to exposure, and exposure to these dangers is cumulative.

This could be the reason that removal of fats, especially animal fats, has been frequently recommended. Maybe it is not

2. Male, O. The significance of mycology in medicine. *in* Hawksworth, D. L., ed. Frontiers in mycology. 1991. C A B International. Wallingford, UK.

3. Cook, Mark. The interface between management and the chicken. 2000. AllTech Symposium. Nottingham Press. UK

simply removing fats from the diet which should be the concern but avoiding the fats of animals exposed to antibiotics, hormones, and grains while enjoying the food products of animals raised according to their natural, healthy, free-range, grass-eating natures.

Early studies said that total fat intake increased the risk of breast cancer, but subsequent analytical studies failed to find that relationship. This "war on fat" was based on far fewer studies than have been done on a substance called conjugated linoleic acid ~ CLA, found in milk and beef fats. Apparently, CLA enhances lean body mass, reduces the size of fat cells, and builds muscle protein.[4, 5] It has also been shown to modulate allergic reactions to foods and to normalize impaired glucose tolerance in noninsulin-dependent diabetics.[4] Recent animal studies revealed that CLA found in milk fat or beef seemed to provide protection from breast cancer. The *Journal of the American Medical Association* (*JAMA*) reports that cancer regresses on a carbohydrate-restricted diet.[6]

So, butter is a health food? The surprising inclusion of fats and eggs in an antifungal diet relates to the fact that **fungi prefer carbohydrates, *not* fats or proteins.** Fungal growth is inhibited by carbohydrate reduction.

The diet's vegetable and fruit restrictions are also simple to analyze. Carbohydrate restrictions include sugars (found in many fruits) and starches (such as wheat flour, potatoes, beans, and rice). These restrictions reduce the fungal load on your immune system and

4. Parodi, P. W. Conjugated linoleic acid: the early years. 1999. in Yurawecz, M. P., Mossoba, M. M., Kramer, J. K. G., Pariza, M. W., & Nelson, G. J. (Eds.) Advances in conjugated linoleic acid research. Vol. 1. AOCS Press. Champaign, IL.

5. Lavillonniere, F., Bougnoux, P. Conjugated linoleic acid (CLA) and the risk of breast cancer. 1999. 276-282. in Yurawecz, M. P., Mossoba, M. M., Kramer, J. K. G., Pariza, M. W., & Nelson, G. J. (Eds.) Advances in conjugated linoleic acid research. Vol. 1. AOCS Press. Champaign, IL.

6. Etzel, R. A. *Mycotoxins*. Jan 23, 2002. 387(4). Journal of the American Medical Association.

aid the effectiveness of the other two prongs of your attack on fungal infection: medications and exercise.

Some foods, however, do have antifungal properties which outweigh their carbohydrate content ~ carrots, yucca (tapioca), and sweet potatoes, for example. These foods contain powerful antifungal properties that are more important to this diet than the amounts of carbohydrates they contain.

Vegetables and fruit are important sources of nutrition. Color is an easy way to assess that nutritional value. Plants make color compounds which protect the plants against the sun's radiation and against microbial infestation. These defenses work to protect people as well. A variety of vibrant, deeply colorful vegetables and fruit[7] provide additional benefits which are outlined in *Vegetables, Side Dishes, and Soups*.

The admonition to buy organic continues to become more important. The chemicals you get from vegetables and fruit need to be *phytochemicals*, not pesticides. Growers are using ten times more pesticides now than 60 years ago. In today's nutritional culture, "organic" is generally used to imply that plants are grown without the use of pesticides, chemical fertilizers, or genetic modifications and animals are 1.) given no antibiotics or hormones and 2.) fed according to their natural inclinations: pasture, free-range, or non-farm-raised fish.

Always *avoid* meats from *grain*-fed animals since they often contain antibiotics, hormones, and pesticides from animal feeds and/ or veterinary practices. Antibiotics and growth hormones encourage fungal growth. Mycoses (fungal infections) have increased since the 1960s because of antibiotics, hormonal contraceptives, *steroids*, and immunosuppressants (such as chemotherapy and anti-rejection drugs used in organ transplants).[2]

----

7.   Joseph, J. A. Nadeau, D. Underwood, A. The color code: a revolutionary eating plan for optimum health. 2002. Hyperion. NY.

Meat, in general, is included in the diet. Considerations in meat and dairy choices are related to how the animals were raised. It is important to include organic sources to minimize exposure to hidden antibiotics and hormones. Look for sources of grass-fed beef, organic meat, free-range poultry, and non-farm raised fish.

Beef cattle are routinely fed grains both while being raised and while in crowded feed lots in preparation for slaughter. Grass and hay, not grains, are the natural food for cattle. Beef cattle incompletely digest grain, which sets up a condition in the bovine stomachs for multiplying the acid-tolerant species of E-coli bacteria. The bacteria are then passed to the human consumer through the meat. These E-coli bacteria are not eradicated by inadequate internal temperatures of the meat nor by human stomach acid, which makes the consumer vulnerable to E-coli infection.

Avoid corn-fed fish and meat. Corn can contain *aflatoxin B1* ~ a mycotoxin and the most carcinogenic substance in the world.[8] Corn and most other grains are high in carbohydrates. Also, field and storage conditions make it difficult to avoid fungal infestation. Additionally, foods prepared from grains often contain sugar. Taken individually, each of these realities invite proliferation of fungi. Added together, it should be obvious why grains, in general, should be avoided.

The current emphasis on weight reduction has increased the pressure for commercial non-caloric sweeteners. An overview of these products (aspartame [NutraSweet™], sucralose [Splenda™], etc.) points up both the rush to tap into the money to be made and the shocking disregard for the well-being of the consumer. You will find more information about the current sweetener situation in the following diet pages.

---

8. Cheeke, P. R. Natural toxicants in feeds, forages and poisonous plants. 1998. Interstate Publishers, Inc. Danville, IL.

Good nutrition builds *immunity*. The *Life Change* Diet reduces the fungal load on your system so an improved immunity can overcome the fungal assault. These restrictions are quite different from the standard American diet.

New Thinking About Shopping

With a new way of eating comes a new way of shopping. Throughout this book you will find suggestions for items to store in your pantry, freezer, and refrigerator that will save you time and money. You will find recommendations for such things as freezing soup stock, working with spices, and preparing items ahead of time.

Some foods on the list of recommendations are foods we seldom use, such as celeriac and yucca. We have included several recipes to help you get started using these healthful food alternatives.

Stevia may be new to you, too. It is a plant whose leaves are 100 to 400 times sweeter than sugar, so follow the suggested usage carefully. Honey is currently being reinvestigated as a valuable antimicrobial addition to a healthy diet. As this research continues, we advocate using honey with discretion in the *LifeChange* Diet.

New Processes and Procedures

There are many measures you can take to reduce your encounter with fungus and other microbes. The home food preparer is urged to learn new processes in food preparation. For example, the need to wash produce has been known for years, but we recommend a relatively new product in washing fruit, Nutribiotic® GSE® ~ a liquid grapefruit seed extract. Grapefruit seed extract is a natural antimicrobial that is non-toxic (*see Processes and Sources*).

Food dehydration is the world's oldest method of food preservation. With the prevalence of modern kitchen appliances such as stoves, refrigerators, and freezers, the dehydration of foods became used almost entirely by commercial food establishments.[9] As we become interested in healthful foods, we can join the group of people who value food dehydration and can benefit from their reservoir of knowledge and extensive experience. (*see Sources* for information on the dehydrator cookbook.)

Today, with reliable electric dehydrators, the process is experiencing a revival. Dehydration is easier and more beneficial than canning. Dehydrated foods have a long shelf life and a very long freezer life. They retain more nutrients since the process does not use extreme heat or water.[9] Buying seasonal, organic foods to dehydrate can save money and build a healthful food supply for convenient meal preparation.

The changes in food selection are outlined in the following diet. The restrictions are relatively simple, though their impact is considerable. The recipe chapters and meal planning suggestions are designed to encourage a well-rounded, sustainable approach to eating. Including new items and processes may require a learning curve, but such learning is definitely worth the effort.

---

9. Bell, Mary. Mary Bell's complete dehydrator cookbook. 1994. William Morrow and Company, Inc. NY.

The LifeChange Diet

An antifungal diet holds a basic dichotomy: there are foods to avoid and foods to include. The often-heard complaint about antifungal dieting is the difficulty with acceptable meal planning, especially for occasions which involve snacking, "brown-bagging," or entertaining. The foods to avoid are easily listed, though they make considerable impact on normal food choices.

Food choices for the *LifeChange* Diet are built on the understanding that fungi's impact creates a broad list of health problems. Fungi are troublesome due, in part, to these characteristics:

1. Fungal cells have nuclei just as human cells do. This is in contrast to bacterial cells which have no nuclei. Antibiotics are mycotoxins (fungal poisons) which kill bacteria, both good (such as intestinal microbes) and bad (such as *streptococci*). The difficulty lies with creating antifungal medications that do not harm the human component. *Viva* the non-toxic role food can play!

2. The *conidia* (disease-causing fungal spores) can hide in cells undetected for years. When these spores are awakened they clone themselves and infection results.

3. Fungi are spoiled and bossy...they prefer carbohydrates which they will take from what you eat for their own life and growth. Reducing the carbohydrate load reduces the fungal load (*see Introduction*).

4. Studies have reported for over 40 years that strong-colored vegetables have a positive effect on health and the immune system (*see* "The Color Code" in *Sources*). These effects are both immune builders and microbe killers (*nutraceuticals*) and have been shown effective even against cancer. A common disclaimer often

accompanies these studies: "The mechanism is unknown." Our conviction is that the antifungal properties of these strong-colored vegetables *are* this causal "mechanism." *Viva* the "food fight!"

Food is one major "army division" in the battle for good health. Its immunity-building and nutraceutical fungi-killing make it an essential partner to exercise and medication for victory over fungally-caused disease. So, let's look at The *LifeChange* Diet.

The *LifeChange* Diet at the *Basic Level* is the approach to conquering microbial assault on the human body. Conquering fungi is often a protracted effort. If your symptoms subside with the *LifeChange* Diet, you have diagnosed your problem. The *Step·Up* recommendations are ways to incorporate the less-detrimental foods back into your diet to test your body's response. If symptoms return, go back to the *Basic Level*. In some places, special recommenda-tions are given for those battling cancer to help with their often-flagging appetites.

Since this battle can go on for extended periods of time, even years, we have planned this approach to be sustainable. Do not get impatient; appreciate every improvement. You will notice a gradual return to natural eating habits which will include a curb of the overwhelming cravings for sweets and carbohydrates.

It is important to also incorporate exercise and, possibly, medication into your regimen. Consider the recommendation to have a health care provider monitor your progress.

Beverages

The best and most beneficial beverage is water ~ either filtered or from a pure spring source. Flavor the water with sweet herbs, vegetables, or juices from allowable fruits to add variety (*see Flavored Waters*).

INCLUDE ~

> filtered water
> fruit-"ades" from allowable fruits; sweetened with *stevia*, if desired
> herbal teas from non-fruit sources
> lemon water, hot or cold

Note: Use glass or lexan® bottles to avoid the potential detrimental effects of plastics. Lexan® bottles are sold in most sporting goods stores or catalogues.

AVOID ~

> coffee and tea, regular and decaf
> herbal teas from fruit sources
> soft drinks, regular and diet

Condiments and Vinegars

This category is mainly related to condiments. Commercial products contain such ingredients as corn syrup, chemicals, and the almost ever-present "natural flavorings." Unfortunately, "natural flavorings" has a wide definition of ingredients we would refuse if plainly listed. (For an illustrative detailed listing, see www.kosherquest.org[10])

Make your own pickles, mayonnaise, mustard, catsup/ketchup, or other desired condiment to ensure a healthy product.

INCLUDE ~
   black olives packed in water
   Bragg's Liquid Aminos
   unpasteurized *apple cider vinegar*

AVOID ~
   pickles, catsup/ketchup, prepared mustards, barbecue sauce, Worcestershire sauce, hot sauces, *soy* sauce, green olives, prepared horseradish, dips and salsas, commercial mayonnaises and salad dressings

Note: Most of these products are fermented or contain fermented ingredients; many of them also contain sugars and/or unallowed oils.

10.   www.kosherquest.org/bookhtml/FOOD_ADDITIVES.htm   January 2004.

Dairy and Dairy Products

Butter and cream are low-carbohydrate foods ~ tasty additions to one's diet. Organic dairy products are healthier beyond their low-carb advantage. In an interview with professor Mark Cook, University of Wisconsin-Madison, he related that grass-fed cattle produce 500 percent more of the essential fatty acid CLA than conventional cattle.

INCLUDE ~
> *butter*
> *feta cheese* from goat or sheep's milk
> goat yogurt
> *heavy cream*
> real-cream *cream cheese*
> real-cream *sour cream*
> *yogurt*, unsweetened

Note: Organic products are best. Goat milk products are a good choice since most goats are raised without the use of anti-biotics or hormones.

AVOID ~
> margarine and all butter substitutes
> milk: whole, 2%, skim, due to the high-carbohydrate count
> non-dairy or dairy-free products
> products with these dairy terms on their ingredient labels

buttermilk	lactalbumin
buttermilk solids	lactalbumin phosphate
casein	sodium caseinate
caseinate	whey

Eggs

Eggs vary in size and taste. Organic eggs (free range) contain higher amounts of omega-3. The problem can be availability.

INCLUDE ~
eggs: organic, from free-range chickens

AVOID ~
all egg substitutes

Grains

INCLUDE ~
See *Breads* for vegetable and nut flours to use in recipes as substitutes for grain flours.

AVOID ~
ALL. Grains tend to be high in carbohydrates and are subject to fungal infestation during storage.

Step-Up Level

Add to INCLUDE these whole grains ~

amaranth	millet
barley	oats
brown rice	quinoa
buckwheat	*real* sour dough (contains no yeast)

Note: Sourdough bread, toasted, should be used on a trial basis. At the first sign of returning symptoms, delete it from your diet.

Herbs and Spices

Herbs and spices add flavor, and flavor is your friend. There is great value even in small amounts of herbs. Rosemary, sage, and thyme, for example, have antioxidants, antimicrobials, and micro-nutrients which have benefits for any consumer but especially the cancer patient. The traces of *phytochemicals* which combine synergistically from even very small amounts of herbs are as valuable to health as a large dose of any one herbal component.[11]

See *Processes* for suggestions on how to preserve them.

allspice	lamb's quarters
angelica	lavender
anise	lemon balm
apple mint	licorice
balm (*Melissa officinalis*)	marjoram
basil	mint
borage	nutmeg
burdock root (tea)	oregano
burnet (cucumber flavor)	paprika/paprica
caraway	parsley
cardamom	peppercorns (black, white, red)
cassia	peppermint
celery seed	pimento
chervil	rosemary
chicory	saffron
chive	sage
cilantro/coriander	spearmint
clove	tarragon
cumin	thyme
dry mustard	turmeric
fenugreek	
ginger	
horseradish root	

11. Joseph, J. A. Nadeau, D. A. Underwood, A. The color code: a revolutionary eating plan for optimum health. 2002. Hyperion. NY.

Meats

Meat is an important source of protein in this diet. As previously discussed, locate an organic source as a more healthful way to include meat in you diet.

INCLUDE ~
>grass-fed, free-range
>>beef
>>bison
>>lamb
>>mutton
>>poultry
>fish

Note: Be sure you the source of your fish. Farm-raised fish is corn-fed fish.

AVOID ~
>cold cuts
>lunch meats
>meats of any kind, including fish, which are breaded or were grain-fed, corn-fed, antibiotic- or hormone-treated

Note: There is some concern in current literature regarding mercury contamination of fish.

Nuts and Seeds

Nuts are a powerhouse of beneficial fiber, food constituents, minerals, protein, vitamin E, cholesterol-lowering phytosterols, and cancer-fighting ellagic acid.[2] All these and great taste, too!

See *Processes* for washing nuts with GSE to eliminate fungal contamination and give nuts a freshly-picked taste.

Some of the stars are:
>   walnuts, for omega-3 oils and higher contents of ellagic acid
>   brazil nuts, for selenium
>   almonds, for riboflavin and vitamin E

INCLUDE ~
>   most varieties, such as pecans, walnuts, pumpkin seeds, sesame seeds, sunflower seeds, brazil nuts, pine nuts, *flax seed*, cashews

AVOID ~
>   peanuts - commonly infected with *aflatoxin* B1
>   pistachios

Sweeteners

INCLUDE ~

stevia - An intensely sweet plant. Stevia has zero calories and is considered a medicinal herb in Latin American countries.[12]

honey - A sweetener that is controversial with diet promoters interested in carbohydrate reduction, though we feel it is an acceptable sweetener.

Interestingly, honey has been used since antiquity as medicine. In the early 20th century, about 60 to 80 years after the 1835 discovery that microbes (fungi) cause disease,[13] honey was studied extensively for antimicrobial use as well as wound healing properties. In the mid-20th century, the focus shifted away from honey to antibiotics. Interest in the antibmicrobial properties of honey has revived during the past 20 years.[5]

Among its nutrients, honey contains antioxidants, phytochemicals, essential amino acids, and antimicrobial factors.[14]

AVOID ~

products with these terms on their ingredient label

corn syrup	maltodextrose
dextrose	maltose
fructose	maple syrup
glucose	sucralose
lactose	sucrose

sugar - A sweet crystalline carbohydrate; sucrose.[15] Fungi harvest useful energy from carbohydrates obtained as nutrients from their environment.[16]

aspartame - Contains aspartic acid, an excitotoxin.[17] An excitotoxin is a neurotransmitter that can cause cell death, including the death of brain cells.[18]

AVOID, continued ~
saccharin - Made from coal tar. Its use is now restricted because it can cause cancer in experimental animals.[18]

sucralose - Chlorinated sugar. Commonly known as Splenda™, sucralose is relatively new and not widely studied. Dr. Mercola's website reports that the chlorine in sucralose is more like that in pesticides than in salt, as has been claimed. He also reports negative findings in animal studies, which points to the harm to internal organs and bodily processes such as pregnancy and digestion, including up to 40 percent shrinkage of thymus glands, enlarged liver and kidneys, reduced growth rate, decreased red blood cell count, and spontaneous abortion.[19]

sorbitol - A sugar alcohol. Even small amounts can cause gastrointestinal problems. Michael F. Jacobson, executive director of the Center for Science in the Public Interest, states, "The FDA should require a better label notice on sorbitol-containing products." Sorbitol may cause diarrhea, bloating, and abdominal pain. Is not suitable for children, though it can be found in products frequently consumed by children.[20]

12. Quillin, P. Beating cancer with nutrition. 2001. Nutrition Times Press, Inc. Tulsa OK.
13. Jenson, B. Anderson, M. Empty harvest. 1990. Avery Publishing Group Inc. Garden City Park, NY.
14. National Honey Board. Honey: therapeutic qualities. www.nhb.org. October 2003.
15. The American heritage dictionary. 1982. Houghton Mifflin Company. Boston.
16. Moore-Landecker, E. Fundamentals of the fungi. 1996. Prentice Hall. Upper Saddle River NJ.
17. Stoddard, M. N. The deadly deception.
18. Thomas, C. L. ed. Tabor's cyclopedic medical dictionary. 1997. F. A. Davis Company. Philadelphia.
19. www.mercola.com. October 2003.
20. Center for Science in the Public Interest. Newsroom. Sept. 27, 1999.

Vegetable Oils

It is preferable to use cold-pressed oil. Good vegetable oils contain omega-3 and other micro-nutrients. We recommend always using organic sources.

We question the use of canola oil. The oil is extracted from the rapeseed plant and is best used in industrial applications. It requires further processing to make it marketable for human consumption.[21, 22] Based on our research, we do not advocate the use of canola oil.

Include ~
for cold preparations:
flax seed oil
grape seed oil
olive oil
sesame seed oil

for high-heat processes, use tropical oils:
coconut oil/shortening
palm oil

Avoid ~
canola oil
corn oil
cottonseed oil
partially-hydrogenated oil
peanut oil
safflower oil
*soy*bean oil[23]

21. Cheeke, P. R. Natural toxicants in feeds, forages and poisonous plants. 1998. Interstate Publishers, Inc. Danville, IL.
22. Enig, M. G. Aug 2002. *in* www.mercola.com. December 2003.
23. Enig, M. G. Fallon, S. W. The oiling of America. www.westonaprice.org. December 2003.

Vegetables and Fruit

The admonition to buy organic is becoming more important. It pays to shop farmers' markets, co-ops, or buying groups and to even grow it yourself. Organic produce is safer for you and encourages a healthier planet.[24]

The use of dehydration (*see Processes and Sources*) can help you take advantage of foods in season and preserve those foods in a healthy way. Dehydration is easier than canning and will preserve more of the healthful food constituents.[25]

Vegetables

Include ~ most vegetables and their juices:

aloe vera	celery
arugula (roguette)	chicory
artichokes	collard greens
asparagus	cress
banana peppers	water
beets	upland
beet greens	cucumber
bell peppers (sweet green and red)	dandelion greens
	eggplant
broccoli	endive
Brussels sprouts	escarole
cabbages, all	fennel (finoccio)
capers, without vinegar	garlic
carrots	kale
cauliflower	kohlrabi
celeriac (celery root)	

~ continued, pg. 22

- - - - - - - - - -

24. Joseph, J. A. Nadeau, D. Underwood, A. The color code: a revolutionary eating plan for optimum health. 2002. Hyperion. NY.

25. Bell, M. Mary Bell's complete dehydrator cookbook. 1994. William Morrow and Company, Inc. NY.

Vegetables to Include, continued

leeks	sprouts
lettuces, all	alfalfa
okra	bamboo
onion	bean
parsnip	squash, all including
pumpkin	chayote
radish	winter
rhubarb	summer
rutabaga	yellow
sea vegetables	zucchini
agar-agar	pepino (melon pear)
carrageen (Irish moss)	sweet potatoes*
dulse	Swiss chard
kelp (sea weed)	tomatillo
sea kale	tomatoes, all
shallots	turnip greens
spinach	yucca (tapioca)

Note: Sweet potatoes are commonly called "yams," though they are not the same plant. (*see "Sweet Potatoes" in Vegetables*)

Avoid ~
legumes/beans/peas
white potatoes

Step-Up Level

Add ~ legumes (beans and peas) to included vegetables

Avoid ~ white potatoes

Fruit

Include ~
avocados
berries, including blueberries, cranberries, loganberries,
       raspberries, strawberries, etc.
cherries
Granny Smith apples
grapefruit
lemons
limes

Avoid ~
all other fruit

Additional Cancer Recommendations

Add to the *Basic Level* list any fresh unblemished fruit, such as bananas and watermelon, fresh fruit juices, or dehydrated fruits. This can help to encourage the cancer patient's appetite.

Yeast Products

Products which utilize yeast in production are using fungi as an integral part of the product. These products are best avoided.

AVOID ~
> ALL. Common products include breads and other bakery goods, mushrooms, alcohol, tofu, miso, or tempeh ~ but this is NOT an exhaustive list.

Note: Hydrolyzed yeast is an additive in many products such as canned and powdered soups and frozen dinners.
> *Watch for it*!

Learning the LifeChange Lifestyle

Due to the life changes you will be making, plan to stock your kitchen pantry and refrigerator, even the freezer, so you can enjoy the learning time, menu planning, and experimentation.

Include in your planning the products for dehydration of vegetables, fruit, and meats. Turkey, chicken, steaks ~ the meats of your choice with herbs and spices are all *Basic Level* foods. Search your own favorite recipe books and sources for various ways to fix and embellish these to your liking.

Items to make ahead

Berry Jam, pg. 143
Bev's Bread and Butter Pickles, pg. 117
Boiled Dressing, pg. 126
Homemade Mayonnaise, pg. 127
LifeChange Mustard, pg. 132
Roasted Garlic, pg. 116
Tangy Catsup, pg. 125

Items to keep in the pantry

dried, unsweetened allowed fruit
dried vegetables
flax seed when whole and untreated
garlic
gelatin, unsweetened, unflavored
honey, local to your area when possible
onion
spices, organic where possible (*see Diet*)
stevia
sunflower seeds
tapioca flour
vanilla extract, organic

Items to keep in the freezer

berries ~ blueberries, cranberries, raspberries, etc.
cherries
flax seed (*see* **Processes**)
meat, stored in useable portions
nut flours, organic when possible
sesame seeds
stock ~ chicken and beef
vegetables, chopped, stored in useable portions for egg
         dishes, entrées, or unsandwiches

Items to keep in the refrigerator

apple cider vinegar
arrowroot
butter
cherry and blueberry concentrate (*see* **Sources**)
ground *flax seed* and flax seed oil
fresh fruit and vegetables

A Beginning Grocery List for
The Sample Week of LifeChange Living

Dairy:

butter   sour cream
eggs   yogurt, organic
heavy cream

Fruit and Vegetables / Produce:

asparagus   eggplant
basil   garlic
beets with green tops   Granny Smith apples
bell pepper, green and red   grapefruit
blueberries ~ fresh and frozen   jicama
broccoli   lemons
Brussels sprouts   lettuce
cabbage, green and red   onions ~ green, sweet, yellow
cabbage slaw, prepackaged   parsley
carrots   spinach
cauliflower   squash ~ butternut, spaghetti,
celeriac   zucchini
celery   strawberries
cherries ~ fresh and frozen   sweet potatoes
cherry tomatoes   tomatoes
chives
cucumber

Meats:

fresh bacon, organic to eliminate nitrites (**not** sugar cured)
beef, ground, organic when possible
chicken, organic when possible
salmon or tuna, water packed
Italian sausage, organic to eliminate nitrites
whole turkey, organic when possible

Miscellaneous:

almond flour/meal
almond milk
almonds, slivered
arrowroot
baking soda (*see Processes*)
black olives, water-packed
blueberry concentrate *
Bragg's Liquid Aminos
cherry concentrate *
chicken broth, organic
cream of tartar

flax seed, ground and whole
honey
sparkling mineral water
stevia, liquid or powder
   or Stevia Plus
tapioca flour
tomato paste, canned organic
   tomatoes, canned
vanilla extract
walnuts
wheat gluten

Oils:

coconut oil
grape seed oil

olive oil

Spices:

allspice
bay leaf
celery seed
cayenne
cinnamon
cloves
chili powder
dry mustard
mustard seeds
oregano

paprika
pepper, ground red
peppercorns
sage
scallions
tarragon
thyme
turmeric

* *see Sources*

A Sample Week of LifeChange Living

Day 1

Breakfast
Scramble Omelet
Blueberry Muffins
fresh berries of your choice

Lunch
Molded Salmon or Tuna salad
fresh vegetables with Fresh Vegetable Dip

Dinner
Chicken with Grapefruit and Tarragon
green salad
steamed broccoli and cauliflower
Molded Grapefruit Salad
Blueberry Yogurt Soup

Day 2

Breakfast
Garden Frittata
Popover Gems with Strawberry Jam

Lunch
Chicken Aspic Salad
fresh vegetables with Fresh Vegetable Dip

Dinner
Sloppy Joes
green salad
Cherry Gelatin with Granny Smith apples

Day 3

Breakfast
Fluffy Pancakes with *Berry Syrup*
fresh berries of your choice
yogurt, sweetened with *stevia* or *Strawberry Jam*

Lunch
homemade chicken soup (*see Processes*)
Crispy Flatbread
leftover *Cherry Gelatin*

Dinner
oven-roasted turkey (leftovers used for *Day 4* and *Day 5 Lunch*)
Baked Sweet Potatoes
LifeChange Cranberry Sauce
Beet Hash
Sauteed Brussels Sprouts
Blueberry Gelatin with *Stabilized Whipped Cream*

Day 4

Breakfast
1-2-3 Crepes with *Berry Syrup*
fresh fruit with *yogurt*

Lunch
turkey *unsandwiches*
fresh vegetables with *Fresh Vegetable Dip*
LifeChange Cranberry Sauce
leftover *Blueberry Gelatin* with *Stabilized Whipped Cream*

Dinner
Vegetable Stew
Crispy Flatbread
Strawberry Bavarian Pie

Day 5

Breakfast
Omelet 101
Blueberry Muffins
fresh grapefruit

Lunch

homemade turkey soup with stock made from *Day 3* turkey
Flax Seed Crackers or *Popover Gems*
leftover *Cherry Gelatin*

Dinner
LifeChange Italian Sausage Spaghetti with
spaghetti squash
Tasty Cabbage Salad
Bev's Custard

Day 6

Breakfast
Blueberry Pancakes with *Fruit Rave*
and *Creme Fraiche*
Granny Smith apple slices with a squeeze of lemon juice

Lunch
Dinner Frittata
Carrot Salad

Dinner
baked salmon with *Basic Level Fish Sauce*
Tomato Aspic
Tangy Coleslaw
Fantasy Yogurt Cheesecake

Day 7

Breakfast
>	*Walnut Pancakes* with leftover *Fruit Rave* (from *Day 6*)
>	and cream

Sunday Dinner
>	*Crisp Baked Lemon Chicken*
>	*Roasted Asparagus*
>	*Boiled Beets with Sautéed Beet Greens*
>	*Sautéed Brussels Sprouts*
>	*Waldorf Salad*

Supper
>	chicken salad *unsandwiches* (use planned-overs from noon
>	or your favorite recipe for chicken salad; substitute
>	allowed condiments and vegetables)
>	*Mock Potato Salad*
>	leftover *Waldorf Salad*

Chapter Two

Vegetables, Side Dishes, and Soups

And God said, "Look.
I have given you the seed-bearing plants throughout
the earth and all the fruit trees for your food."
~ Genesis 1:29 TLV

We are creatures of habit. We have our personal sets of vegetables and side dishes we draw from to plan our meals. Often the foods we prepare include potatoes and grains and sugars in the forms of breads and pastas. Planning for dinner without potatoes, grains, and sugar, though not difficult, will bring changes. We have discovered a multitude of flavorful dishes drawn from unique preparation methods to assist in your new choices.

Vegetable recipes abound ~ in every cookbook and on a wide variety of cooking shows. Adapt them creatively to fit your favorites into the allowed foods list. Use the appropriate list of allowed vegetables from the *LifeChange* Diet and refer to *Processes* for simple, economical preparation tips. Choices of vegetables should come from organic sources to reduce your intake of pesticides and herbicides.

It is important to wash purchased produce. We recommend the use of grapefruit seed extract (*GSE*®) to cleanse vegetables and fruit of external fungi and impurities. This also extends the life of the produce. Nuts, when washed and dried, taste fresher. See *Processes* for directions for this procedure.

Processes will also discuss how to make your own soup stock. Soups provide a warm, comforting, healthy way to enjoy vegetables and meats. They can save time and money as you utilize leftovers. Soups contain the water soluble minerals and vitamins normally discarded during food preparation. They can bring warmth in colder months then be a lighter, cooler meal for the warmer months.

Spices and herbs can serve to add flavor-interest to food preparation as well as health benefits. They have a wide influence on main dishes, vegetable dishes, salads, and even desserts. We suggest that you research your own cookbooks or go to the library to enlarge the place herbs and spices have in your cooking. There are also some useful ideas in *Tips*.

Asparagus

Asparagus is usually seen in spring when it is most tender and plentiful, although in today's produce market, it can be available almost all year. It is best to buy asparagus not by the bunch but by the pound. Choose stalks of similar diameter, large or small, whose bottoms look fresh and have no splits or scaling. Store them like fresh flowers, standing up in about one inch of cold water in a jar in the refrigerator. Asparagus is a good source of potassium and folic acid and also has vitamins A, B, and C.

You can eat asparagus raw as well as boiled, roasted, or grilled. Cut or snap off the lower ends at the point where they snap easily, the rest will be tender.

When serving asparagus raw, wash the spears very well then cut or snap off the tough ends of the stalks. Raw asparagus makes a unique and delicious addition to tossed green salads. It can also be a last minute addition to an egg fritatta or used to decorate other vegetable salads.

Experiment by making your own asparagus brunch salad. Top the raw spears with a crumbled boiled egg, crumbled cooked bacon, chopped chives, and *LifeChange Hollandaise, Fresh Basil Mayonnaise*, or your own favorite brunch ingredients.

Steamed Asparagus

Cut or snap off the tough ends where they break naturally.
Rinse the spears.

Lay the spears in a 10 to 12 inch diameter skillet or sauce pan fitted
with a steamer basket. Add ½ inch or so of boiling water. Cover
tightly and steam for 3 to 5 minutes or until almost tender; the asparagus will continue to cook a little as it cools.

Remove the asparagus and steamer basket from the pan and spread
the asparagus out on a towel to cool slightly.

See serving suggestions under *Boiled Asparagus*.

Boiled Asparagus

Cut or snap off the tough ends where they break naturally.
Rinse the spears.

In a 10 to 12 inch diameter skillet or sauce pan, lay the spears on
their side. Add water to almost cover; add a sprinkling of salt. Bring
to a boil, then lower heat to a simmer.

Test the asparagus after 4 minutes for desired tenderness. When
barely tender, drain and dry on kitchen towels.

Serve warm with a little butter, *Orange Mayonnaise*, or try warm
Boiled Dressing to which you've added your choice of *Roasted
Garlic*, curry, cilantro, chives, *Horseradish Cream*, or other seasoning
which complements your meal.

Roasted Asparagus and Red Peppers

1 lb asparagus, trimmed and fibrous stalks removed
1 large red bell pepper, seeded and cut into ½ inch strips
1 tbsp fresh lemon juice
1 tsp *olive oil*
½ tsp salt
⅓ tsp crushed red pepper, to taste
1 tsp grated lemon *zest*

Preheat oven to 400 degrees. Spray baking sheet with *nonstick spray*.

In a large bowl, combine asparagus and red bell pepper strips. Add lemon juice, olive oil, salt, and crushed red pepper. Toss well to coat.

Arrange vegetables on baking sheet. Bake for 15 to 18 minutes or until tender. Shake pan occasionally during cooking.

Transfer vegetables to serving bowl. Toss with the lemon zest.

Serves 4

Roasted Asparagus Vinaigrette
This is very easy and turns out rather "gourmet-ish."

1 large clove garlic, peeled, minced
2 tbsp *apple cider vinegar*
½ tsp dry mustard
6 tbsp extra-virgin *olive oil*
salt and freshly-ground black pepper, to taste
1 lb asparagus (12 to 18 medium thick spears) cleaned, fibrous
     stalks removed

Preheat oven to 400 degrees.

Lightly oil a rimmed baking sheet or 9x13 inch baking dish. Set
aside.

Prepare vinaigrette: in small bowl, combine garlic, vinegar, and
mustard. Whisk in oil until completely emulsified. Season with salt
and pepper to taste.

To roast asparagus: Drizzle vinaigrette over asparagus and turn to
coat well. Arrange asparagus in single layer on an oiled baking sheet
or baking dish.

Roast for 15 minutes or until tender and lightly browned. Shake the
pan a few times during cooking for even browning.

Serves 4

Beets

The official value of beets is both general and specific. Red beets provide vitamins A and C, calcium, iron, and fiber to your diet. There are only 25 calories in one half-cup of plain, diced beets. Beets add powerful color to make meals more enjoyable. There is also evidence that strong-colored vegetables have anti-cancer properties. Epidemiological research indicates that high fruit and vegetable consumption is associated with lower cancer risk.[1] Dr. Patrick Quillin, a nationally known cancer nutritionist, declares the necessity of good nutrition in the treatment of cancer. In his rating of foods, beets are included in his list of "best" foods to have in the diet.[2]

My dear neighbor, Carol McBroom, is one of those unofficial "good cooks." Carol has wonderful memories of beets served from the garden when she grew up in Missouri. She has increased my appreciation of this colorful vegetable. She chided me one day for discarding the beet greens. Now I value the greens as a chopped element in scrambled eggs or omelets and include them as greens in a salad.

Beverly

----

1. Kohlmeier, L. Simonsen, N. Mottus, K. Dietary modifiers of carcinogenesis. 103(8). 177-184. Nov 1995. Environmental Health Perspectives.

2. Quillin, Patrick. Beating cancer with nutrition. 2001. Nutrition Times Press, Inc. Tulsa, OK.

Baked Beets

1 medium or ½ large beet per person
heavy cream

Scrub beets. Bake in 375 degree oven in ovenproof glass dish for
45 minutes.

Remove beets from oven and cool to the touch. Rub the cooked
beets with a paper towel to remove the skins, then grate the beets
using the large holes on the grater.

Divide grated beets into individual serving dishes. Top each with
1 to 2 tablespoons of cream, either whipped or unwhipped, or use in
Apple and Beet Side Dish.

Note: Use 2 medium beets for 1 cup of grated beets.

Apple and Beet Side Dish

2 tbsp *butter*
1 medium-to-large Granny Smith apple, peeled, cored, and grated
          (about 1 cup)
½ C chopped onion
1 C grated *Baked Beets*
½ tsp salt
dash each of pepper and nutmeg

Melt butter in a medium saucepan. Add apple, onion, beets, and
seasonings. Mix, cover, and heat thoroughly. Serve hot.

Serves 4

Roasted Beets

4 medium beets, trimmed of stems and roots, scrubbed
2 tsp *olive oil*
1 tsp *apple cider vinegar*
1 garlic clove, minced
½ tsp fresh ground pepper
½ tsp salt
water

Preheat oven to 375 degrees.

Spray a baking pan with *non-stick cooking spray* or add just
enough water to barely cover bottom of pan to prevent sticking.
Stand beets in pan; leave room between each. Bake until tender
when pierced with tip of knife, about 1 to 1½ hours.

Let cool; remove skins. Cut into wedges and place on serving plates.
In a small bowl, combine olive oil, vinegar, garlic, pepper, and salt.
Whisk until well combined. Thin with water until desired consis-
tency. Drizzle over beets.

Serve warm or at room temperature.

Serves 4

Beet Hash

2 medium beets, peeled
2 Granny Smith apples, peeled, cored, and diced into small cubes
juice of 1 lemon
1 large *celeriac*, peeled and cut into small cubes
1 small butternut squash, peeled, seeded, and cut into small cubes
4 tbsp unsalted *butter*
1 medium onion, sliced into rings
salt to taste plus more for water
freshly ground black pepper, to taste
2 tbsp fresh flat-leaf parsley, coarsely chopped

Heat oven to 475 degrees.

Wrap beets in aluminum foil. Bake until a knife easily pierces beets, about 45 minutes. Let cool 1 hour.

Meanwhile, prepare the apples, celeriac, and squash. Toss apple cubes with the lemon juice.

Bring a large pot of salted water to a boil. Prepare an ice-water bath. Blanch celeriac for 2 minutes, transfer to ice-water bath to stop the cooking process, then drain in a colander. Repeat this process for the butternut squash.

In a heavy skillet over medium-high heat, melt butter until bubbling. Add onion and cook until softened, about 2 minutes.
 Add celeriac and cook 2 minutes.
Add squash and cook for an additional 2 minutes.
Add beets and apples; cook, stirring, until all ingredients are tender, about 3 more minutes. Season to taste.

Remove from heat; sprinkle with parsley and serve.

Serves 6 - 8

Boiled Beets with Sautéed Beet Greens

If you are able to find a fresh bunch of beets with nice, fresh leaves, don't waste them. Beet greens are just as delicious as beets themselves. Serve the two together to get the best of both worlds.

Virginia

½ tsp salt, plus more to taste
3 lbs medium beets, greens removed and washed
1 tbsp *olive oil*, plus more for drizzling
1 clove garlic, thinly sliced
freshly ground black pepper, to taste

Fill a large sauce pan with water, set over high heat, and bring to a boil. Stir in salt, add beets; boil until beets are fork-tender, about 45 minutes. Drain, let cool, and rub off skins under cold water.

Heat olive oil in a large skillet over medium heat. Add garlic and cook until just golden, about 3 minutes. Add beet greens and season with salt and pepper. Cook, tossing greens just until wilted. Remove skillet from heat.

Serve warm greens with whole boiled beets. Drizzle with additional olive oil, if desired.

Serves 6 - 8

Broccoli

The champion cruciferous vegetable! You can eat the stems as well as the florets. Broccoli is thought to have strong anticancer compounds. It is also strong in vitamins A and C as well as calcium, phosphorus, potassium, and zinc.

Choose broccoli with tightly closed buds, a fresh smell, a bright green color, and firm, tender stalks. Avoid broccoli with yellowing leaves or flower buds or with stalks that are thick, woody, or whose ends are split. Store broccoli unwashed in a perforated plastic bag in your refrigerator's vegetable crisper. It should be used in two or three days.[3]

Wash broccoli well immediately prior to use (*see Processes*). Peel the stems and cut them into one-half-inch pieces, then cook for three minutes before you add the florets. Four or five minutes more and the broccoli should be done ~ firm but tender. Serve them warm with lemon butter or toss with *Roasted Garlic*, roasted bell peppers, or cooked, shredded celeriac.

When adding broccoli to cold salads, blanch it first by boiling for just two minutes, then drain and rinse immediately with cold water. This brightens the color of the broccoli and develops the flavor.[1]

You can also eat broccoli raw ~ cut up in a green salad, as a last minute addition to an egg frittata, or serve with other fresh, sliced veggies as an appetizer or on a buffet with *Fresh Vegetable Dip* or *Tomato-Basil Dip*.

3. www.maxlabs.com/hn/Food_Guide/Broccoli.htm   January 2004.

Easy Broccoli and Garlic with Spaghetti Squash

1 medium spaghetti squash
1 tsp salt
2 tbsp *butter*
4 tbsp *olive oil*
3 cloves garlic, finely chopped
3 C broccoli florets
3 tbsp water

Preheat oven to 350 degrees.

Cut the squash in half lengthwise and remove the seeds. Place cut side down in a roasting pan. Add enough water to cover the bottom of the pan and cover with foil. Bake about 50 minutes or until fork tender.

Shred the cooked spaghetti squash with a fork and place the strands into a large mixing bowl. Toss in the salt and butter and set aside.

Heat a heavy skillet over medium heat. Add olive oil and garlic; watch to be sure garlic does not stick or scorch. When garlic has browned slightly, add broccoli and water and stir continuously until broccoli is tender, about 10 minutes. If needed, add a little more water. When broccoli is tender, add it to the bowl of spaghetti squash and toss lightly to combine.

Lightly toss in additional olive oil, *Garlic Oil,* or *Parsley Oil* if the vegetables seem a little dry.

Serves 4 - 6

Orange-Broccoli Side Dish
A *Cancer Recommendation* recipe.

1 small head broccoli, washed, peeled, and cut into small cubes
1 small head cabbage, washed and finely shredded
zest and juice of 1 large orange
2 tbsp *honey*
$\frac{1}{4}$ C *apple cider vinegar*
1 tbsp *olive oil*
$\frac{1}{4}$ C toasted chopped walnuts

Place prepared broccoli and cabbage into a large mixing bowl.

Whisk together the orange zest and juice, honey, vinegar, and olive oil. Pour over vegetables. Chill for several hours or overnight.

To serve, toss in the toasted walnuts.

Serves 6 - 8

Curried Broccoli

6 C fresh broccoli florets
½ lb *bacon*, cooked and crumbled
½ C onion, diced
½ C dried cherries, coarsely chopped
¾ C *LifeChange Boiled Dressing*
1 tsp curry powder
½ C sunflower *seeds*, toasted

Preheat oven to 325 degrees. Spray a large glass casserole dish with *non-stick spray*.

In a large mixing bowl, combine the broccoli, bacon, onion, and cherries.

In a separate bowl, whisk together the *Boiled Dressing* and curry powder. Pour over the vegetable mixture and toss to coat. Bake 20 minutes or until broccoli is tender.

To serve, top with toasted sunflower seeds and serve warm.

Serves 6 - 8

Brussels Sprouts

Brussels sprouts are miniature cabbage-like vegetables which bear the name of the capital city of Belgium.
Unfortunately they have acquired a dismal reputation. While
Brussels sprouts are never mild tasting, much of their reputation for strong flavor comes from the fact they are almost
always overcooked. Like all cruciferous vegetables, Brussels sprouts contain chemicals which, when heated, produce sulfur. With gentle heating, the vegetable takes on a
pleasing peppery, slightly bitter character. Too much heat
however, creates an unpleasant odor and taste.

When sprouts are stored for a long period, they
develop a musty smell and flavor. It is best to buy them as
fresh as possible but frozen Brussels sprouts are a good
alternative. Cook them briefly, just until tender yet still having
a bright green color. Steaming or sautéing are the best
cooking methods for either fresh or frozen.

Because of their assertive flavor, Brussels sprouts are
best served with robust foods such as roasted meats. In
autumn, the freshest Brussels sprouts are sold as they grow:
clustered together on a long stalk. It is more likely you will
find them prepackaged or sometimes loose. Choose
sprouts of similar size to ensure even cooking, and be sure
to look at the sprouts' bases to see that they're not brown or
dried out.

Virginia

Sautéed Brussels Sprouts

1 qt water
1 tsp salt
2 C Brussels sprouts
¼ C *butter* or *olive oil*
1 medium onion, chopped
salt and pepper to taste

Bring water to a rapid boil in a medium sauce pan. Add salt and
Brussels sprouts. Cover, return to a gentle boil, and cook until
sprouts test tender crisp when pierced with a sharp knife, about
4 minutes. Drain well.

In a medium skillet, sauté the chopped onion in melted butter until
tender. Add the warm, drained sprouts and season to taste. Toss
gently until thoroughly heated.

Serves 4

Brussels Sprouts with Bacon and Apples

coarse salt
24 oz Brussels sprouts, trimmed and halved lengthwise
8 oz *bacon*, cut into ¼ inch pieces
1 Granny Smith apple, peeled, cored, and cut into ¼ inch dice
¼ tsp fresh thyme leaves
freshly ground pepper

Bring a large pot of water to a boil and add salt. Add Brussels sprouts and cook until sprouts are tender and bright green in color, about 6 minutes. Do not overcook.

Cook bacon in a large skillet over medium heat until the fat renders and bacon is crisp, 2 to 3 minutes. Drain excess bacon grease. Add apples and cook, stirring occasionally, until apples are golden brown, 2 to 3 minutes. Add thyme and season with pepper.

Using a slotted spoon, add Brussels sprouts to skillet. Taste and adjust seasoning as desired. Serve immediately.

Serves 4

Brussels Sprouts with Vinegar-Glazed Red Onions

1 tsp salt
1 10 oz package of Brussels sprouts
1 tbsp unsalted *butter*, divided
1 tbsp *olive oil*, divided
freshly ground black pepper
1 small red onion, thinly sliced lengthwise
2 tbsp *apple cider vinegar*

Bring a medium pot of water to a boil and add salt. Prepare an ice-water bath.

Trim outer leaves and stems from sprouts, discard. Add Brussels sprouts to boiling water, cook until tender but still bright green, about 4 minutes. Remove from heat, drain, and plunge into ice-water bath to cool. Drain well and cut sprouts in half from stem to top.

Heat half the tablespoon of butter *and* half the tablespoon of olive oil in a large, heavy skillet over medium-high heat. Add Brussels sprouts, cook, tossing occasionally, until they are brown and crisp on the edges, about 3 minutes. Season to taste with salt and pepper and transfer to a large bowl. Cover with aluminum foil to keep warm.

Add remaining half-tablespoon of butter and oil to the same skillet over medium-low heat. Add onions, cook, tossing occasionally, until wilted and transparent, about 3 to 4 minutes. Add vinegar (stand back to avoid the fumes) and stir to loosen any brown bits on the bottom of the pan. Cook until vinegar is reduced and the onions are glazed, about 30 seconds.

Add onions to Brussels sprouts. Toss well. Serve immediately.

Serves 4

Cabbage

Another cruciferous anticancer vegetable hero, cabbage has vitamins A and C, phosphorus, and folic acid. It comes in green or red and is also known as Savoy and Chinese cabbage. Each of the varieties is high in fiber.

Look for firm heads that feel heavy. They will keep for about a week in the refrigerator. To reduce its strong smell, keep cooking times brief or serve it raw.

Sautéed Cabbage

Sliced cabbage sautéed in *butter* and tossed with a little *heavy cream* and snipped dill is delicious.

Curried Cabbage

Mix mild curry powder with *butter* to sauté sliced cabbage. Cover and cook for several minutes or until tender. Add salt and pepper to taste.

Steamed Cabbage

Place cabbage wedges in a steamer basket. Place basket in a sauce pan containing 2 inches water. Bring to a boil, cover, reduce the heat slightly, and cook for 3 to 4 minutes. Be careful not to overcook. Toss with *butter*, paprika, salt, and pepper.

See additional cabbage recipes in *Salads*.

Carrots

Unlike other low-carbohydrate diets, carrots should be included in dieting for health. Carrots have significant *carotenes*, beneficial *phytochemicals*, vitamins, and fiber. A number of studies show carrots to be an anti-cancer, anti-fungal, stroke-preventing, cholesterol-lowering food. Carrots are valuable as a side dish or a snack.

Beverly

Sautéed Carrots

3 tbsp *butter*
2 C grated carrots
¼ tsp salt
¼ tsp ginger
chopped parsley for garnish

Melt butter in a medium sauce pan. Add carrots, salt, and ginger. Cover and cook over medium heat until tender-crisp, stirring occasionally, about 5 minutes.

Place in a serving dish, garnish with parsley.

Serves 4

Carrot Puff

2 tbsp *butter*
1 C onions, minced
2 C diced carrots
1 *egg*, separated
¼ tsp salt
dash of ground cloves
lemon, cut into wedges, for garnish

Preheat oven to 350 degrees. Butter a 5 x 9 inch glass loaf pan.

Melt butter in small skillet over low heat and sauté onions until tender.

Steam carrots until just tender, then place in a blender container. Purée. Transfer puréed carrots to a mixing bowl. Add egg yolk to puréed carrots, beat until smooth. Add sautéed onions to the purée.

In a separate mixing bowl, beat the egg white until stiff. Fold into carrot mixture. Add salt and ground cloves.

Spoon mixture into prepared loaf pan. Bake 20 to 25 minutes. Serve hot with a lemon wedges.

Serves 4

Cauliflower

Cauliflower is another of the cruciferous vegetables loaded with vitamin C and some iron. This vegetable can be prepared in the same way as broccoli. An added bonus is that cauliflower can also do a stand-in for potatoes in stovetop preparations.

Cauliflower Purée

Steam cauliflower florets or microwave them until soft. Purée in a food processor or food mill. Add *butter* and *heavy cream* to taste. Season with salt and pepper and warm briefly in a saucepan. Serve as a substitute for mashed potatoes.

Sautéed Cauliflower

Steam florets and then sauté them lightly in *olive oil* mixed with minced garlic and diced red bell pepper.

Hazelnut Brown-Buttered Cauliflower

Cauliflower's mild but distinctive flavor is enhanced with a sauce of brown butter with roasted hazelnuts. Be sure to monitor the butter carefully so that it browns but does not burn.

1 C *hazelnuts* (*filberts*)
3 small or 2 large heads cauliflower
10 tbsp unsalted *butter*
2 tbsp freshly squeezed lemon juice
2 tbsp snipped chives

Preheat oven to 350 degrees.

Place hazelnuts on a baking sheet and toast until fragrant, about 10 minutes. Remove nuts to a kitchen towel; rub off loosened, papery skins. Coarsely chop nuts; set aside.

Trim cauliflower stems so they sit flat; keep the cauliflower head intact. Bring several inches of water to a boil in a large steamer or in a pot fitted with a rack; add salt to taste. Steam cauliflower until just tender, about 20 minutes. Transfer to a platter.

In a medium saucepan, melt butter over medium heat. Add skinned, chopped hazelnuts. Cook until butter turns brown, 3 to 4 minutes. Remove from heat and add lemon juice and chives. Season with salt and stir to combine. Pour over cauliflower and serve immediately.

Serves 8 - 10

Celeriac

The rough, deep brown exterior of celeriac makes it look like the surface of the moon, for it is channeled with nubs, crevices, and hairy rootlets. Once the queen of the root cellar, it was practically banished from the North American diet when refrigeration appeared and the graceful, slender, pale-green-stalked, cultivated celery became favored in the U.S.

Europe, however, never lost its preference for this root vegetable. Cultivated in the Mediterranean, it was introduced to Britain in the 1700s and is grown throughout Europe. It is a favorite in the Orient and India, as well. The Netherlands devotes a significant amount of their export agriculture to celery root. Three-quarters of their crop is exported, and the remainder is either processed or sold locally on the fresh market. The long-time famed bistros of France serve time-honored Celeriac Remoulade.

Celeriac (pronounced celery'-ack) mystifies many. It is related to parsley but not to the celery we are more familiar with; in fact, it is more like celery's first-cousin-once-removed. Celeriac bears many names, such as celery root, celery knob, and German celery.

Celeriac is a good source of potassium, phospho-rous, and vitamin C, with small amounts of vitamin B, cal-cium, and iron. It has been credited with boosting the im-mune system. Though high in sodium, it is rich, filling, high fiber, fat-free, and cholesterol-free.

Select roots slightly larger than softballs, heavy for their size, and as smooth as possible. A good one will be firm with a distinct aroma of celery.

Basic Celeriac

To prepare, always wash well (*see Processes*) and peel celeriac using a sharp knife rather than a potato peeler. The interior is smooth and white, similar in texture to a radish or white turnip root. Once peeled, cut into coarse chunks or shred.   Can be used raw in salads.

Cooking Suggestions

~ Boil celeriac and mash with butter and herbs.
~ Steam, braise, grill, or deep fry one-half inch thick slices.

Potential Uses

~ Substitute for celery or for potatoes in salads, soups, stews, or
       casseroles
~ Combine with watercress, beets, carrots, turnips, or parsnips
~ Excellent in poultry or meat stuffings
~ Add fresh herbs, nutmeg, garlic, cinnamon, cloves, allspice, or
       cilantro to enhance flavor

Hot Celeriac Soufflé

1 *celeriac* root
4 C water
1 tsp salt
3 *eggs*, beaten
³/₄ C *heavy cream*
¹/₂ tsp thyme
salt and pepper, to taste

Preheat oven to 325 degrees. Butter a deep casserole or soufflé dish.

Peel the celeriac and cut it into ³/₄ inch cubes. Bring water to a boil, add salt and cubed celeriac. Boil for 10 to 15 minutes or until very tender. Drain well.

Gently purée the celeriac using a blender or food processor on a slower speed. Pour purée into a mixing bowl. Add eggs, cream, thyme, salt, and pepper. Mix well.

Transfer mixture to the prepared dish. Place soufflé dish into a larger pan and add water to the larger pan until the water level reaches 2 inches. Bake for 45 to 50 minutes or until set.

Turn out soufflé onto serving dish. Drizzle with *Aioli* or other cream sauce of your choice. Serve as a side dish with roasted beef or chicken.

Serves 4

Celeriac Remoulade

A traditional French recipe with a light lemon cream sauce we have adapted from *The Heritage of French Cooking*.

To cook the celeriac:
1 *celeriac* root, about 1½ lbs
3 tbsp lemon juice
salt

For the sauce:
1 *egg* yolk
1 tsp dry mustard
⅓ C grape seed oil
salt and freshly ground pepper
1 tbsp lemon juice
2 tbsp *cream*

Peel the celeriac. In a food processor or by hand, cut the celeriac into fine julienne pieces.

In a large nonaluminum saucepan, bring 2 inches of water to a boil, add the lemon juice and a pinch of salt. Add the celeriac. Return water to a boil and remove from heat. Drain the celeriac and refresh under running water. Drain again in a strainer, then dry with a cloth.

Prepare the sauce. Whisk the egg yolk and mustard together in a bowl. Continue whisking as you add the oil in a thin stream until it becomes a thick mayonnaise. Add salt, pepper, and lemon juice and mix again. Mix in the cream and continue to whisk until the sauce is creamy.

Place the celeriac in a large bowl. Add the sauce and mix well. Refrigerate until ready to serve.

Serve individual portions sprinkled with freshly ground pepper.

Serves 6

Celeriac in Olive Oil
A Middle Eastern version.

1 *celeriac*, peeled and cut into ¾ inch cubes
2 tbsp extra-virgin *olive oil*
juice of half a lemon or more to taste
¼ tsp turmeric
1 tsp *honey*
salt and pepper

Gently sautée cubed celeriac in the olive oil until lightly browned. Add water to cover and stir in lemon juice, turmeric, honey, salt, and pepper.

Simmer about 25 minutes or until the celeriac is tender and the liquid is considerably reduced.

Serve hot or cold.

Serves 4

Eggplant

Eggplant contains saponins and pectin which are helpful in reducing cholesterol. Along with tomatoes, bell peppers, and onions, eggplant contain substances which help fight asthma. New evidence suggests that when eaten in a diet rich in fruit and vegetables, it may even help prevent skin wrinkling.

Aubergine is the French name for eggplant, which is native to southern and eastern Asia and has been cultivated since antiquity. It's extremely popular in Creole, Middle Eastern, and Mediterranean cuisine.

The large, egg-shaped fruit can vary in color from a deep purple to red to yellow or white. It is the white coloring and its shape that gives it its popular name. All varieties have the same delicious flavor and can be prepared the same way.

Size ranges from tiny to the 1½ to 2 pound oval eggplants found in most American markets.

Chefs sometime salt eggplant before cooking to draw out its bitter taste. Unfortunately this will neutralize the beneficial saponins. Use fresh organic eggplants from a farmer's market or purchase Japanese eggplant. These varieties will not need to be salted.

Eggplant Side Dish

This salad is delicious as a dip, a spread, or a side dish

1 large eggplant
1 medium sweet onion, peeled and chopped
3 tbsp lemon juice
1 tbsp minced garlic
½ tsp salt, or to taste
¼ tsp pepper, or to taste
¼ tsp cumin
dash of chili pepper

Roast whole eggplant at 350 degree F. for 1 hour. Peel and run through a food processor with all the other ingredients.

Serves 4

Baked Eggplant Creole

A *Step-Up Level* recipe. For *Basic Level* recipe, do not use the rice.

1 medium eggplant (about 1½ lbs)
½ lb ground beef (round or chuck)
1 clove garlic, crushed
¼ C onion, finely chopped
¼ C green bell pepper, cored, seeded, and finely chopped
½ C celery, finely chopped
1 can (1 lb) tomatoes, undrained
¼ tsp dried thyme
2 tsp salt
dash red pepper flakes
1 C brown rice, cooked

Preheat oven to 375 degrees. Lightly butter the inside of a 2-quart ovenproof casserole. Wash eggplant under cold running water; cut off and discard the stem end. Cut eggplant into 1 inch cubes.

Pour water in a large sauce pan to measure 1 inch deep and bring to a boil over high heat. Add eggplant cubes to the boiling water. Cover and simmer for 10 minutes or until eggplant is tender. Drain well and set aside to cool.

In a large skillet, brown ground beef and garlic over moderate heat, stirring constantly to break up the meat. Add onion, green pepper, and celery; sauté 5 minutes longer. Add tomatoes with their liquid, thyme, salt, red pepper flakes, and drained eggplant. Bring to a boil over high heat; reduce heat to moderately low and simmer, uncovered for 10 minutes, stirring frequently.

Mix cooked brown rice to eggplant mixture, toss gently to combine thoroughly. Turn into greased casserole dish. Bake, uncovered for 15 minutes or until hot and bubbly around the edges of the dish.

Serves 6

Tomato Ratatouille Sauté

3 large (about 1½ lbs) fresh tomatoes
1 tbsp *olive oil*
1 C onion, chopped
1½ tsp garlic, minced
2 C zucchini, sliced
2 C eggplant, diced
2 C green bell pepper, cut into chunks
½ C water
¼ tsp salt
1 tsp basil leaves, crushed
¼ tsp thyme leaves, crushed
¼ tsp ground black pepper

Core tomatoes and chop coarsely ~ makes about 4 cups. Set aside.

Heat a large sauce pan over medium heat; add oil, onion, and garlic. Cook and stir until softened, 3 to 4 minutes. Add zucchini, eggplant, and green pepper. Cook, stirring until slightly softened, about 2 to 3 minutes.

Add water, salt, basil, thyme, black pepper, and prepared tomatoes. Bring to a boil; reduce heat and simmer, covered, until vegetables are tender, about 15 minutes, stirring occasionally.

Serve over cooked spaghetti squash for *Basic Level*, or over cooked brown rice for *Step-Up Level*.

Serves 4

Grilled Red Onions

2 tbsp *apple cider vinegar*
1 clove garlic, minced
1 ½ tsp fresh rosemary, chopped
1 tbsp *olive oil*
2 lb red onions, peeled
salt and pepper, to taste
½ C fresh parsley, chopped

Heat vinegar, garlic, and rosemary in a sauce pan until hot. Do not boil. Let stand 20 minutes. Warm the oil in a separate pan.

Slice the onions into ½ inch slices. Lay them out on a cookie sheet and brush both sides with warmed oil. Sprinkle with salt and pepper. Grill the onions until slices are slightly charred, 3 to 4 minutes. Remove from grill and separate into rings.

Toss grilled onion rings with the vinegar mixture and fresh, chopped parsley.

Serves 6

Squash

As a child, the name "squash" made me turn up my nose. Then, as a young preacher's wife, I prepared the squash which church members brought to our home. I quickly learned to enjoy squash!

Summer squash is a general term for thin-skinned yellow or zucchini squash. Winter squashes are more thick skinned with potato-like flesh and can be a great substitute for potatoes. Winter squashes, though sometimes boiled, are more typically baked. Some common varieties are acorn, butternut, Hubbard, pumpkin, and spaghetti, however, new varieties are appearing in the grocery stores every day.

Flavor summer squash as you would potatoes in a "top of the stove *mélange*" of squash and onions. Spaghetti squash can easily replace its pasta counterpart. Enjoy!

Beverly

Baked Acorn Squash

2 acorn squash
2 tbsp *unsalted butter*
½ tsp *stevia*
¼ tsp maple flavoring
½ tsp cinnamon
¼ tsp nutmeg

Heat oven to 350 degrees.

Cut the squash into halves and remove the seeds. Cut a slice off each piece so they will sit flat, skin side down, in a 9 x 13 inch glass baking dish.

Melt the butter, stir in stevia and seasonings. Drizzle mixture over the squash. Bake until fork-tender, about 45 minutes.

Serves 4

Pumpkin Casserole

Adapting the pie recipe on the label of a can of pumpkin serves as a delicious vegetable entrée.

1   2 lb can of pumpkin
½ C *honey*, divided
¼ tsp liquid *stevia*
1½ tsp cinnamon
⅛ tsp ground cloves
½ tsp nutmeg
½ tsp ginger
¾ tsp salt
3 *eggs*, separated
1 C *heavy cream*, scalded

Preheat oven to 325 degrees.

Mix pumpkin, honey, and stevia, reserving one tablespoon honey. Add the spices and salt, egg yolks, and scalded cream.

Whip the egg whites with the reserved honey. Fold into the pumpkin mixture.

Pour into a greased loaf pan. Bake until set in the center, about 35 minutes.

Serves 4

Spaghetti Squash

An interesting substitute for pasta.

1 spaghetti squash (2½ to 3 lb)
½ C *olive oil*
6 cloves garlic, chopped
¼ tsp red pepper flakes
⅓ C water
¾ tsp salt
¼ tsp black pepper
 dried oregano to taste

Preheat oven to 350 degrees.

Cut the squash in half lengthwise and remove seeds. Place cut side down in a roasting pan. Add enough water to cover the bottom of the pan and cover with foil. Bake about 50 minutes or until fork tender.

Heat oil in a saucepan. Add garlic and pepper flakes, cook one minute or until garlic just **begins** to color. Add water, salt, and black pepper. Bring to a boil and add the oregano a bit at a time until seasoned to your taste.

Shred the cooked spaghetti squash with a fork and place the strands into a large mixing bowl. Add the garlic mixture and toss.

Serves 6

Squash Casserole

2 lbs yellow squash or zucchini (older, larger squash may be used
        here), cleaned and cut into ½ inch rounds
1 yellow onion, peeled and diced
1 tbsp plus 1 tsp coarse salt, divided
1½ C ground nuts, any type desired, divided
3 large *eggs*, lightly beaten
1 C *heavy cream*
1 tsp fresh thyme leaves
8 oz *cream cheese*, softened, divided
1 tsp freshly ground black pepper
pinch cayenne pepper

Preheat oven to 350 degrees.

Place squash and onion in a medium sauce pan and cover with
water. Add 1 tablespoon salt and bring to a boil. Reduce heat and
simmer until tender, about 20 minutes. Drain well, transfer to a large
bowl.

To the squash, add 1 cup nuts, eggs, cream, thyme, 4 ounces softened
cream cheese, black pepper, cayenne pepper, and remaining salt.
Gently stir to combine. Pour into a 2 quart shallow baking dish.

Spread remaining 4 ounces softened cream cheese and remaining
nuts over the top. Cover and bake until set, about 30 minutes.
Uncover and continue baking until top is browned, about 10 minutes
more.

Serves 8

Stuffed Squash

3 (about 3½ lbs total) Hubbard squash
2 tbsp *honey*, divided
1 tbsp *olive oil*
1 large onion, finely chopped
1 large rib celery, thinly sliced
1 Granny Smith apple, cored and cut into ¼-inch cubes
⅓ C dried unsweetened cherries
¾ C chicken *broth*
¾ tsp salt
¼ tsp ground cinnamon
1 tbsp *arrowroot*
½ C walnuts, toasted

Preheat oven to 400 degrees. Coat jelly-roll or other baking pan
which has sides with *nonstick spray*.

Cut squash in half lengthwise, remove seeds. Brush each cut side of
squash with 1 tablespoon honey, total. Place squash, cut side down,
on pan. Bake 30 to 35 minutes or until fork-tender.

In a nonstick skillet, heat oil over medium heat. Add onion and
celery; cook 3 minutes. Add apple, cherries, broth, salt, cinnamon,
and arrowroot. Bring to a boil. Lower heat to medium; cover.
Simmer 12 to 15 minutes or until liquid is absorbed. Stir in walnuts.

Reduce oven temperature to 375 degrees. Turn squash halves cut
side up. Fill each squash with about ½ cup stuffing. Drizzle with
remaining honey.

Serves 6

Variation: For individual servings and a dramatic presentation,
hollow out 6 small whole acorn or calabaza squash. Bake,
cut side down and proceed as above.

Sweet Potatoes

Most people are unaware of the difference between yams and sweet potatoes. The vegetables labeled "yam" in American markets actually are sweet potatoes. Related to the morning glory, sweet potatoes come in a variety of colors ranging from yellows to purple.

True yams are gigantic roots which are not related to sweet potatoes. They are found most often in tropical locations. Neither sweet potatoes nor yams are related to white potatoes.

The wonderful sweet potato stars as a delicious, health-giving vegetable. The Center for Science in the Public Interest ranks sweet potatoes first among a large group of vegetables relative to vitamins A and C, folate, iron, copper, calcium, and fiber. Additionally, sweet potatoes have *carotenoids* and cancer-fighting constituents, like quercetin.[4]

Mashed sweet potatoes are a good side dish or a healthy way to add moisture and volume to *Basic* or *Step*Up Level* modified quick bread recipes. Boiled cubed sweet potatoes or mashed sweet potatoes can also be used as a pasta substitute on which to serve meat entrées and sauces.

— — — — — — — — — —

4.   Joseph, J. A. Nadeau, D. Underwood, A. The color code: a revolutionary eating plan for optimum health. 2002. Hyperion. NY.

Mashed Sweet Potatoes

1 qt water
1 tsp salt
2 lbs sweet potatoes, washed
¼ C *butter* or *olive oil*
salt and pepper to taste

Bring water to a rapid boil in a large sauce pan. Add salt and sweet
potatoes. Cover, return to a gentle boil, and cook until potatoes are
tender when pierced with a sharp knife, about 20 to 25 minutes.
Drain well.

Transfer boiled sweet potatoes to a large mixing bowl. Use a potato
masher or wooden spoon to mash potatoes to desired consistency.
Stir in butter or olive oil, salt, and pepper to taste.

Serves 4 - 6

Variation: Use as a base on which to serve *Lemon-Orange Rosemary Chicken, Basil Roasted Chicken with Garlic Sauce*, or
LifeChange Italian Sausage Spaghetti, or experiment with
your own meat/vegetable/sauce combinations.

Baked Sweet Potatoes

2 lbs sweet potatoes, washed
2 C *stock* (turkey, chicken, or vegetable)
½ C *honey*
2 - 3 tbsp *butter*
1 clove garlic
1 medium onion, sliced
1 rib celery, chopped
2 or 3 carrots, sliced thinly into rounds

Preheat oven to 350 degrees.

Peel the sweet potatoes and cut into 1 inch rounds. Place in a baking dish.

Warm the stock. Add the honey and butter and stir. Pour over the sweet potatoes.

Place garlic, onion, celery, and carrots into the dish with the sweet potatoes. Bake until tender, basting periodically.

Serves 4

Yucca

A member of the lily family, yucca is native to the southwestern United States and Mexico. Also known as cassava, tapioca, or manioc, it is the seventh-highest production food in the world and is the diet staple for over 500 million people worldwide. Yucca is high in vitamins A and B-complex as well as vitamin C, calcium, potassium, phosphorous, iron, manganese, and copper.

We believe any vegetable that lowers cholesterol is anti-fungal. Yucca has been used for hundreds of years for its natural healing properties ~it is a major source of saponins. Saponins have potential as both medications and dietary additives for use in lowering cholesterol levels in humans.[5] Information from the field of microbiology shows that sterols, from which cholesterol is made, are probably produced by all fungi.[6] Combine these two facts and it is obvious why yucca (tapioca) should be included in an antifungal diet.

Today the high potency, naturally occurring saponin proves beneficial for arthritis, inflammation, some forms of cancer, and lowering blood pressure and cholesterol levels ~ all with no detrimental side effects. Researchers speculate that yucca saponin's are effective against arthritis and inflammation because they block the intestinal release of toxins into the blood stream which inhibit normal formation of cartilage. The saponins also help in the reduction of stress and swelling and work to detoxify the body.

---

5. Cheeke, Peter R. Natural toxicants in feeds, forages and poisonous plants. 1998. Interstate Publishers , Inc. Danville, IL.

Though used, primarily, in the *LifeChange* Diet as a grain substitute, yucca can also be used as a side dish. *Tapioca flour*, used in *Breads*, is another form of this same plant and provides a healthy way to include some comfort foods back into the diet (*also see "Tapioca Flour" in Processes*).

Basic Yucca

To cook yucca, use a sharp knife to cut into 3 to 4 inch sections. Stand each section on end and cut away the thick, bark-like skin. Cut the section into quarters lengthwise and remove any hard core. Place yucca pieces in a medium sauce pan, cover with water, and bring to a low boil for about 20 minutes or until fork tender.

The boiled yucca is an excellent substitute for baked white potatoes ~ or mash the boiled yucca and add butter, cream, salt, and pepper. Experiment!

6. Moore-Landecker, E. Fundamentals of the fungi. 1990. Prentice Hall. Englewood Cliffs, NJ.

Garlicky Yucca

1 medium *yucca*
¼ tsp salt
¼ C *heavy cream*
2 tbsp *olive oil*, divided
4 cloves garlic, minced
juice of ½ lime
black pepper
ground red pepper (optional)

Use a sharp knife to cut yucca into 3 to 4 inch sections. Stand each section on end and cut away the thick, bark-like skin. Cut each section into quarters lengthwise and remove any hard core. Place yucca in a saucepan and cover with water; add salt and stir. Bring to a simmer and reduce to low heat. Simmer 25 to 35 minutes, until tender when pierced.

Add the cream and heat, but do not let it boil. Drain well. Dice the yucca into bite size cubes.

Warm 1 tablespoon olive oil in a non-stick skillet over medium heat. Add minced garlic and diced, cooked yucca. Cook while tossing until yucca starts to brown. Remove from heat. Drizzle with remaining olive oil and sprinkle with lime juice. Season with peppers, as desired.

Serve as browned pieces with *Fresh Vegetable Dip*.

Serves 2 - 4

Variation: Reserve the creamy liquid in which the yucca was simmered. After dicing the yucca into cubes, use the reserved liquid to mash the yucca and serve with your favorite toppings.

Soup

A warm and welcome comfort food with so much potential as an appetizer or main dish. Preparation ahead of time makes soup a hearty saver of both time and money.

Have the components ready ahead and you will have soup almost as fast as opening cans but with added food value. See *Processes* for information on homemade stocks and broths; also for what to have on hand and how to combine them.

Serve with *Crispy Flatbread, Popover Gems*, or *Flax Seed Crackers* along with vegetable sticks for some crunch and you have a comfort meal for sure.

Quick Mug-o'-Soup

Very fast, very tasty, very filling ~ when you're in a hurry or have a cold and need something soothing!

6 oz. fresh vegetable juice or (1) 6 oz. can V-8 juice
6 oz. organic chicken or beef *broth*

Combine in a 12 ounce soup mug and heat for 2 to 3 minutes in the microwave.

Serves 1

Cream of Asparagus Soup

1 lb asparagus, cut into 2-inch lengths
2 onions, chopped
2 tbsp *butter*
2 tbsp *arrowroot* powder
4 C chicken *broth*
½ C *heavy cream*
salt and pepper to taste

In a large soup pot, sauté onion in butter until tender, about 3 minutes. Stir in arrowroot powder until onions are evenly coated. Add chicken broth slowly, while stirring. Add asparagus. Cover and simmer 20 minutes or until asparagus is tender.

Purée mixture until smooth. Add cream, salt, and pepper to puréed soup and reheat. Be careful not to boil the cream mixture. Serve warm.

Serves 4

Sweet Onion Soup

4 medium-sized sweet onions, peeled and sliced
3 medium shallots, sliced
5 cloves of garlic, sliced
1 tbsp *olive oil*
1 tbsp *butter*
1 quart chicken *broth*
¼ C *heavy cream*, if desired

In a large, heavy skillet, sauté onions, shallots, and garlic in olive oil and butter until soft.

Place sautéed vegetables in a blender or food processor container with a little of the broth - add this slowly to avoid splashing the hot mixture. Purée. Combine the puréed onion mixture with the remaining broth in a medium soup pot. Heat.

Stir in the heavy cream, if desired, and return to heat. Be careful not to boil the cream mixture. Salt to taste. Serve immediately.

Serves 4

Variation: Top with croutons made from toasted sour dough bread for a *Step-Up Level* dish.

Hearty Quick-Together Beef Soup
A good way to use leftover roast and vegetables.

1 tbsp *olive oil*
1 medium onion, chopped
2 to 3 C vegetables of your choice, cut into bite-size pieces*[1]
1 large package mixed frozen vegetables (broccoli, cauliflower,
        or carrots)
1 package frozen chopped spinach
1 32 oz. jar tomato juice or tomato juice-based vegetable juice
1 32 oz. carton organic broth ~ chicken, beef, or vegetable
1 32 oz. water-filled juice jar
3 - 4 C cooked roast or whatever you have leftover, cut into bite-
        size pieces, and its cooking juices
salt, pepper, and seasoning to taste*[2]

In a large soup pot, sauté the onion in olive oil. Add the other
vegetables of your choice; stir to distribute evenly over the bottom of
the pan. Sauté, stirring occasionally, until raw vegetables have just
begun to cook, about 5 to 8 minutes.

Add the frozen vegetables and stir well. Pour in the juice and the
broth, then fill the juice jar with water and pour the water into the
soup; stir to mix well. Bring to a boil then reduce the heat and let the
soup simmer about 15 minutes or until the vegetables are almost
tender. Watch to be sure the level of the liquid stays above the other
ingredients; add additional water or juice as necessary, or you can
also add a can of tomatoes (whole, diced, or stewed) with their
juice.

~ *continued, p. 83*

Cut roast into bite-size pieces and add to the soup along with the meat's cooking juices. Sample the soup broth and season to taste. Simmer another 20 to 30 minutes, stirring occasionally, until all the vegetables are tender and the flavors have mingled. Do not over-cook or the vegetables will become mushy.

Serve with *Flaxseed Crackers*, *Popover Gems*, carrot or celery sticks, or a dollop of plain yogurt and a sprinkle of chopped chives.

Serves 8 - 10

Notes: 1. Other vegetables can include diced butternut squash, eggplant, celeriac, or yucca, sliced carrots, shredded cabbage, chopped garlic, shallots, or bell pepper. If tomatoes are desired, wait to add them with the meat.

2. Possible seasonings include basil, celery seed, cumin, curry, ginger, oregano, paprika, parsley, sage, tarragon, or thyme, depending upon the flavor you desire. This is a good way to experiment with new flavorings.

Roasted Butternut Squash Soup with Crème Fraîche

2 medium butternut squash, cut in half
2 tbsp *butter*
2 cloves garlic, minced
1 yellow onion, chopped
2 Granny Smith apples, peeled, cored, and chopped
1 tbsp fresh thyme, minced
2 tbsp salt
½ tsp fresh ground pepper
2 qts vegetable or chicken *stock* (*see Processes*)
½ C *Crème Fraîche*

Preheat oven to 400 degrees. Cover a baking sheet in aluminum foil.

Place squash, cut side down, onto prepared baking sheet. Bake for 40 to 50 minutes or until knife can easily cut through the flesh. Remove the squash from the oven; let it cool.

In a medium stockpot, melt the butter, add the garlic, onion, and apples. Sauté until onions are tender and clear. Add the salt and pepper and stir well. Simmer for 1 to 2 minutes.

Use a spoon to scoop the seeds from the cooked squash; discard. Scoop out the flesh of the squash and add to sautéed onion mixture. Add stock. Bring to a boil then reduce the heat and simmer for 20 to 30 minutes.

Pour soup into a blender or food processor container. Process for several minutes until smooth; add more stock until it has reached the desired consistency. Serve warm with the *Crème Fraîche* and a sprinkle of fresh thyme.

Serves 4

Variation: Add finely chopped chili pepper; use cilantro instead of thyme.

Chilled Spinach-Yogurt Soup

2 tbsp vegetable oil
1½ C chopped onions
1 *celeriac*, cleaned, sliced, and diced
1 tsp salt
dash of black pepper
1½ - 2 C vegetable *stock* or water
10 oz fresh spinach, washed and stemmed
2 C *heavy cream*
2 - 3 tsp chopped fresh dill, or 2 tsp dried
1 C plain *yogurt*
nutmeg, preferably freshly grated

In a large stock pot, sauté chopped onions in oil over low heat for 10 minutes. Add celeriac, salt, pepper, and stock. Bring to a boil, reduce heat; cover. Simmer for 10 to 15 minutes or until celeriac is tender.

Add spinach. Cook for 2 to 3 minutes or until spinach is wilted but still bright green. Remove from heat. Add cream and dill.

Place in a food processor or blender container and blend until very smooth. If you use a blender, it should be done in several batches. Return to the stock pot or a large covered bowl.

Whisk in the yogurt. Chill for at least 4 hours. The soup will thicken as it cools. If it is too thick, whisk in additional heavy cream that has been mixed with water or add additional stock or water. Adjust seasonings to taste.

Serve garnished with pinch of nutmeg, if desired.

Serves 4

Variation: Use homemade chicken stock. Substitute chopped, fresh cilantro leaves instead of the dill. Garnish with sour cream and additional cilantro leaves for a slightly more Mexican-food flavor.

Chapter Three

Salads

"One has dined well when one has plunged
into the depths of a salad bowl."[1]

Salads usually refer to foods that are crisp and fresh. It is also a term loosely used to refer to rather hearty mixtures of cooked vegetables, meats, or fish which are in reality cold main dishes.

To keep fresh vegetables crisp, store them in a hydrator or wrapped in a damp cloth in the crisper drawer of the refrigerator. Wilted vegetables can be freshened in a pan of cold or ice water until crisp and then drained thoroughly. Vegetables should be washed and drained well both before combining and before the addition of a dressing for a salad (*see Processes*).

Salad items can stand alone to be garnishes for platters. These can include: leaf or head lettuce, celery, cabbage leaves, watercress, parsley, nasturtium leaves, celery leaves or tender curls, or radishes with a bit of the green leaf still on. The garnish is considered part of the salad or main dish and is meant to be eaten.

—————————————————

1. Engstrom, Martha. Grandma's farm country cookbook. 1996. Voyageur Press. St. Paul, MN.

Molded Grapefruit Salad

I found this recipe in an old farmer's wife cookbook. The ingredients intrigued me as they were allowable foods with the substitution of stevia. My extended family and I were surprised at the fabulous taste of this salad. It has a very fresh taste and is very fast to prepare, setting up very quickly.

Virginia

2 tbsp (2 envelopes) gelatin
¼ C cold water
½ C boiling water
1 tsp liquid *stevia*
3 tbsp lemon juice
3 C grapefruit, pulp and juice
½ C chopped walnuts
lettuce leaves, for serving garnish
Homemade Mayonnaise or *LifeChange Boiled Dressing*

Soak the gelatin in the cold water in a mixing bowl for 5 minutes. Dissolve the soaked gelatin and the stevia in the boiling water. Cool.

Add the lemon juice, grapefruit juice and pulp, and walnuts. Let it stand until the mixture begins to thicken.

Mix well and turn into a mold. You may add ½ to 1 cup of fresh or frozen unsweetened berries for color and taste.

Chill. Serve on the crisp lettuce with the *Mayonnaise* or *Dressing*, as desired, on the side.

Serves 6

Waldorf Salad

2 C Granny Smith apples, cored and diced
1 tbsp lemon juice
½ C *LifeChange Boiled Dressing*
1 C celery, diced
½ C walnuts, chopped
⅓ C *heavy cream*, whipped
¼ to ½ tsp *stevia*, liquid or powdered, optional

To prevent discoloration, sprinkle the diced apples with the lemon juice or mix immediately with the *Boiled Dressing*. Add the celery and walnuts.

Add the whipped cream to *Boiled Dressing* then fold into the apple mixture. Stevia may be added with care not to add too much.

Serves 4 - 6

Carrot Salad

2 lbs carrots
½ onion
½ large green pepper, chopped

<u>Dressing</u>
¼ C *apple cider vinegar*
1 tbsp *honey*
⅛ to ¼ tsp *stevia*, to taste
¼ C oil
1 tsp salt
1 tsp *LifeChange Mustard*
1 tsp celery seed

Grate carrots and onion then add chopped green pepper.

In a large mixing bowl, combine the dressing ingredients. Pour over the vegetables and mix well.

Serves 6

Lemon and Asparagus Brown Rice Salad

A *Step*Up Level* recipe. For *Basic Level*, omit the rice.

2 C asparagus (about 10 oz), cut into 1 inch pieces
3 C cooked cold brown rice (from ¾ C raw)
⅓ C fresh mint, finely chopped, packed
¼ C parsley, finely chopped
1 tsp grated lemon *zest*
¼ C fresh lemon juice
1 clove garlic, finely chopped
2 tbsp *olive oil*
salt, to taste
freshly ground black pepper, to taste

Clean asparagus, cut off tough ends of stalks, and cut stalks into
1 inch pieces. Place in a steamer basket over ½ inch of boiling water.
Cover tightly and steam for 3 to 5 minutes or until almost tender; the
asparagus will continue to cook a little as it cools.

In a large serving bowl, stir together cooked rice, asparagus, mint,
and parsley.

In a small cup, stir together the lemon zest, lemon juice, and garlic.
Stir into the rice mixture. Stir in olive oil, salt, and pepper. Cover
and refrigerate up to 2 days.

Let stand at room temperature for 2 hours before serving.

Serves 6

Variations: If you like to experiment, try this recipe substituting any
other *Step*Up Level* cooked, whole grain for the rice.

Molded Cucumber Salad

3 envelopes or 3 tbsp granulated gelatin
½ C cold water
½ C boiling water
⅛ tsp salt
2 tbsp *apple cider vinegar* or lemon juice
1 C grated cucumber

In a mixing bowl, soak the gelatin in the cold water until soft. Add the boiling water and stir until the gelatin is dissolved. Add salt and vinegar and let cool.

When the liquid is cool, add the cucumber. Set in a cool place to thicken.

Serves 4

Dilled Cucumbers

3 cucumbers
¼ C fresh dill
1 C *apple cider vinegar*
¼ C water
4 tsp *honey* or ¾ tsp *stevia*
½ tsp salt
dash of pepper
dill sprigs for garnish

Wash cucumbers and thinly slice. Add snippets of dill. Combine vinegar, water, honey or stevia, salt, and pepper. Stir to dissolve, pour over cucumbers, and lightly mix. Refrigerate to chill for 2 hours or overnight.

Transfer cucumbers from the liquid with a slotted spoon to a serving dish.

Serves 4

Cucumbers in Mint Vinaigrette

3 cucumbers, not peeled
1 tsp salt
¾ C *apple cider vinegar*
¼ C water
scant 1/4 tsp *stevia* or 2 tbsp *honey*
1 clove garlic, minced
1 shallot, minced
2 tbsp chopped fresh mint
2 tbsp minced fresh dill
snipped chives, for garnish

Score the outside of each cucumber with the tines of a fork, then cut cucumbers into thin slices. Place slices in a bowl and sprinkle with salt. Let them stand 1 hour. Use a strainer to drain the liquid from cucumbers then place them in a serving bowl.

Combine vinegar, water, stevia or honey, garlic, shallot, mint, and dill and pour over cucumbers. Cover and chill several hours or overnight. Just before serving, sprinkle with chives.

Serves 4

Cucumber Salad

1 cucumber, peeled and diced
1 large tomato
1 small onion, chopped fine
1 tbsp fresh mint or parsley, minced
1 tbsp *olive oil*
1 tbsp lemon juice or *apple cider vinegar*
1 tsp minced garlic
Salt and pepper to taste

Combine all ingredients. Chill before serving.

Serves 2

Cauliflower-Cabbage Salad

1 head cabbage
1 head cauliflower
1 medium onion
1 lb *bacon*, fried crisp

<u>Dressing</u>:
2 C *LifeChange Boiled Dressing* or *Homemade Mayonnaise*
1 tbsp *honey*
$^1/_8$ tsp *stevia*
salt and pepper to taste
$^1/_3$ C *yogurt*

Wash cabbage and cauliflower well. Slice and chop cabbage; tear cauliflower into small florets. Dice the onion. Combine cabbage, cauliflower, and onion. Chill.

Just before serving, add the bacon and *Dressing*.

Serves 6 - 8

Tasty Cabbage Salad

5 oz slivered almonds
3 tbsp sunflower *seeds*
1 - 2 tbsp of *butter* for sautéeing
2 tbsp *honey*
½ C grape seed oil
1 pkg cabbage slaw, rinsed well
1 bunch green onions, chopped

In a small non-aluminum skillet, sauté the almonds and sunflower seeds in butter over low heat. Watch carefully to prevent burning. Cool.

In a large serving bowl, combine the honey and oil. Add the slaw, onions, and sautéed nuts. Toss together and serve.

Serves 6

Coleslaw

1 head cabbage (about 2 lbs), washed and shredded
¼ C *olive oil*
2 tbsp *apple cider vinegar*, lime juice, or lemon juice
⅛ tsp dry mustard
½ tsp celery seed
2 tbsp *LifeChange Boiled Dressing* or *Homemade Mayonnaise*
¼ tsp *stevia*
salt and pepper, to taste
dash of paprika, to taste

Place shredded cabbage in a refrigerator container with a tight-fitting lid. For extra crunch, soak the shredded cabbage in salt water in the refrigerator for an hour or so, drain, then continue with the following directions.

In a small mixing bowl, combine oil with vinegar or lime or lemon juice. Add mustard, celery seed, *Boiled Dressing*, stevia, salt, pepper, and paprika; mix well. Pour over the shredded cabbage; toss to distribute evenly throughout the cabbage. Cover and refrigerate.

For the best taste, prepare the slaw up to a day ahead so the flavors have time to blend.

Serves 6 - 8

Tangy Coleslaw

1 C plain *yogurt*
1 C *LifeChange Boiled Dressing* or *Homemade Mayonnaise*
1 tbsp *apple cider vinegar*
1 tsp *stevia*
1 tsp salt
½ tsp black pepper
⅛ tsp ground red pepper
8 C shredded green cabbage (about 2½ lbs)
2 C shredded red cabbage (about ½ lb)
2 large carrots, peeled and shredded

In a large mixing bowl, whisk together yogurt, *Boiled Dressing* or *Mayonnaise*, vinegar, stevia, salt, and black and red peppers. Add cabbages and carrots to the dressing in the bowl; stir until completely coated. Cover with plastic wrap.

Refrigerate for at least 1 hour or preferably overnight.

Serves 6 - 8

Skillet Salad

1 slice fresh organic *bacon*
2 C finely chopped cabbage
1 C chopped celery
½ green pepper, shredded
½ small onion, chopped
1 tomato, chopped
optional: red pepper and/or *apple cider vinegar*, to taste

Fry bacon, set aside ~ reserve 1 tablespoon of fat in the skillet.

Put vegetables in the hot skillet and stir over low heat. Add salt and pepper. Cook until tender crisp. Add pepper or vinegar, if desired.

Place in a serving bowl and top with crumbled bacon.

Serves 4

Perfection Salad

2 tbsp (2 envelopes) granulated gelatin
½ C cold water
1½ C boiling water
½ C *apple cider vinegar*
juice of 1 lemon
½ tsp *stevia*
1 tsp salt
2 C finely shredded cabbage
1 C finely chopped celery
¼ C chopped water-packed *black olives*
lettuce leaves, for garnish

In a large mixing bowl, soak the gelatin in the cold water until soft.
Add the boiling water and stir until the gelatin is dissolved. Add the
vinegar, lemon juice, stevia, and salt. Cool.

When the mixture thickens, add the vegetables. Mold and chill.

Serve over a bed of lettuce.

Serves 4 - 6

Celeriac Salad

1 small *celeriac*
$\frac{1}{2}$ tsp allspice
pinch of salt
$\frac{1}{8}$ tsp pepper
$\frac{1}{2}$ C *apple cider vinegar*
1 Granny Smith apple, peeled
$\frac{1}{4}$ C *sour cream*
1 tsp dry mustard

Peel and wash the celeriac then cut into julienne strips.

Bring a pot of water to boil. Add the allspice, salt, and pepper, then the sliced celeriac. Lower temperature and boil until tender, about 10 minutes. Drain the celeriac.

Place celeriac in a mixing bowl. Add the vinegar, toss lightly to coat, and let cool.

Grate the apple into the cooled celeriac. Add the sour cream, dry mustard, and additional salt and pepper to taste. Toss lightly.

Serves 4

Mock Potato Salad

1 large *celeriac*, peeled and cubed
2 hard-boiled *eggs*, grated
¼ C *LifeChange Boiled Dressing*
salt and pepper, to taste

Clean celeriac. Boil celeriac whole in water for 30 to 45 minutes
or until somewhat fork tender. Cool. Peel and cube. Cook cubes
further in water until tender. Drain and cool.

To celeriac, add grated eggs, *Boiled Dressing,* and optional ingredients, as desired. Salt and pepper to taste. Mix well and allow to
cool about 1 hour in the refrigerator.

Serves 4 - 6

optional ingredients: chopped celery, diced onions, dill seasoning,
celery seed, diced bell peppers, or *Bev's Bread & Butter
Pickles*.

Tomato Jelly or Tomato Aspic

A gelled vegetable salad to serve as a side dish for beef, lamb, or chicken dinners.

2 tbsp granulated gelatin
½ C cold water
1 14 oz can tomatoes, do not drain
1 slice of onion
3 cloves
2 peppercorns
¼ bay leaf
1 tsp salt
⅛ tsp *stevia*
2 tbsp lemon juice
lettuce leaves or cabbage slaw
Homemade Mayonnaise or *LifeChange Boiled Dressing*

In a small mixing bowl, soak the gelatin in the cold water.

In a sauce pan, combine the tomatoes with the onion, cloves, peppercorns, bay leaf, salt, and stevia. Cook for 5 to 10 minutes. Use a slotted spoon to remove the cloves, peppercorns, and bay leaf and discard. Pour remainder of tomato mixture into the container of a blender or food processor and purée.

Pour 2 cups of this hot tomato purée over the softened gelatin. Add the lemon juice. Stir until well dissolved.

Wet the molds with water and pour in tomato mixture. Place in the refrigerator until set. Unmold over lettuce leaves or cabbage slaw. Top with *Homemade Mayonnaise* or *Boiled Dressing*.

Serves 4

Chicken Aspic Salad

3 tbsp gelatin
½ C cold water
2 tbsp chopped parsley
2 tbsp chopped onion
¼ C celery leaves
1 qt chicken *broth*
1 tbsp lemon juice
2 C cooked diced chicken
1 C chopped celery
¼ C cooked diced carrots
½ C chopped green pepper
lettuce, parsley, *Homemade Mayonnaise*, or *LifeChange Boiled
Dressing*, for garnish

In a small bowl, soak the gelatin in the cold water.

In a large saucepan, simmer the parsley, onion, and celery leaves in
the chicken broth for 20 minutes. Add the prepared gelatin. Stir
well and place in a large mixing bowl; cool.

When the mixture begins to set, add the lemon juice, chicken, and
vegetables. Pour into one large or several individual molds and chill
thoroughly.

Unmold and garnish with lettuce, parsley, and *Homemade Mayonnaise.*
or *Boiled Dressing.*

Serves 4

Molded Salmon or Tuna

2 tbsp gelatin
¼ C cold water
¼ C lemon juice or *apple cider vinegar*
1 C hot *LifeChange Boiled Dressing*
2 C flaked salmon or tuna
2 tbsp chopped water-packed *black olives*
cabbage slaw or vegetable salad
Homemade Mayonnaise
vegetable sticks for garnish

In a large mixing bowl, combine the gelatin, cold water, and lemon juice and allow the gelatin to soften. Add the hot *Boiled Dressing*, stir until gelatin is dissolved and well mixed. Add salmon or tuna and olives. Pour mixture into a mold and chill well.

Serve with the cabbage slaw or fresh shredded vegetable salad garnished with *Homemade Mayonnaise* and more black olives.

Serves 4

Asian Chicken Salad

2 chicken breasts, cooked, skinned, boned, and shredded
4 C thinly sliced cabbage, Napa or Savoy preferred
1 C grated carrots
4 green onions, white part minced, green part slivered
½ C finely chopped fresh mint leaves
½ C finely chopped fresh cilantro
2 tbsp sesame seeds, toasted

Dressing:
3 tbsp *apple cider vinegar*
2 tbsp *Bragg's Liquid Aminos*
1 tbsp *honey*
2 tsp Asian sesame oil
2 tsp finely grated fresh ginger
½ tsp hot pepper sauce, or to taste

¼ C coarsely-chopped, roasted, salted cashew nuts, for garnish

In a large mixing bowl, combine shredded chicken, cabbage, carrots, green onions, mint, cilantro, and sesame seeds.

In a separate, small mixing bowl, whisk together vinegar, Liquid Aminos, honey, sesame oil, ginger, and hot sauce. Let sit for several minutes to allow flavors to blend.

Drizzle dressing over chicken and vegetables. Toss to combine. Sprinkle with cashew nuts and serve.

Serves 4 - 6

Stuffed Tomato Salad

Allow a whole peeled and chilled tomato for each serving. Using only 3 cuts, slice each tomato from the top almost to the bottom to make 6 sections, so the tomato can be spread apart like a flower.

Fill the center of each tomato with one of the following:
- ~ deviled egg half, crumbled or intact
- ~ *feta cheese*, plain or mixed with cucumber or nuts
- ~ chicken, fish, or meat salad
- ~ mixed vegetable salad
- ~ cabbage salad combination

Deviled Eggs

12 *eggs*
⅓ cup *yogurt*
3 tbsp *LifeChange Boiled Dressing* or *Homemade Mayonnaise*
1 tsp dry mustard
⅛ tsp salt
paprika

Place eggs in a saucepan and cover with water. Bring to a boil for 5 minutes. Turn off the heat and let sit for 10 minutes. Drain and cover eggs with cool water. Let the eggs sit for 15 minutes in cool water.

Peel off the egg shells and cut the eggs in half lengthwise. Place the yolks in a mixing bowl and the whites on a plate. To the cooked yolks, add yogurt, *Boiled Dressing*, mustard, and salt and mash until blended smooth. Spoon the yolk mixture into the cavity of each hard cooked egg white half.

Arrange on a serving platter. Sprinkle with paprika and serve.

Makes 2 dozen

Chapter Four

Condiments & Dressings

Dressings, sauces, gravies, and dips ~ the culinary elements that turn ordinary meals into extraordinary events. To prepare them yourself insures health-promoting interest in your menu planning. Make *Basic Level* provision for mayonnaise, mustard, dressings, and other condiments to avoid carbohydrates and fermentations.

Since we most often think of seasonings when preparing sauces and dressings, this would be a good place to have a word about the rich arena of herbs, seeds, and oils. Today we understand that herbs, seeds, and oils pack powerful antiviral, antibacterial, and antifungal properties. Seasonings are not only tasteful but healthful.

We want to enjoy flavorful foods, but we often resist the difficulties involved in stocking special herbs, seeds, and oils. Often we just stop using those flavor-adding treats due to the time, money, or waste involved. I, too, am frustrated when a specific flavoring is not in my spice cabinet or I am not sure where to find it ~ or when I find an old container of it which needs to be thrown away! In *Processes* we cover recommendations for the proper storage of a variety of spices and flavorings.

Salad dressings contain only a few essential ingredients: acids, fats, and seasonings. Acids might be in the form of vinegar or lemon juice. Fats take the form of vegetable oil, olive oil, butter, or meat drippings. Seasonings run the gamut from salts and peppers to paprika, garlic, mustard, water-packed/non-fermented capers, thyme, tarragon, and a wealth of items in

between.[1] A basic rule of thumb for *Basic Level* dressings is:
3 parts *olive oil* plus 1 part *apple cider vinegar* or lemon juice.

Salad dressings are generally categorized by how the fat is treated in the recipe. Emulsifiers serve to bind substances together which normally would not combine, such as oil and water. Emulsifying is most obvious in sauces, dressings, and baked goods. Examples of emulsifiers in recipes include the lecithin in eggs, butter, or mustard.

The treatment of the fats determines whether the fat is in a temporary emulsion, a permanent emulsion, or emulsified by cooking. These groups are illustrated by

1. a vinaigrette with ingredients that separate in the serving container (temporary emulsion),

2. mayonnaise with a familiar creamy consistency from an interaction of the ingredients (permanent emulsion), and

3. boiled dressing with a creamy consistency from heating the ingredients in a double boiler (applied heat emulsion).

Each has a special place in your healthful meal preparations.

Although olive oil is the primary oil listed in our dressing recipes, feel free to experiment with various other oils including grape seed, flax seed, coconut, sesame, sunflower, walnut, and different varieties of olive oils. ***Beware of canola oil*** ~ it is not made from a canola! (*see Glossary* and "*Vegetable Oils*" in the *Diet*.)

---

1.   Engstrom, Martha, ed. Grandma's farm country cookbook. 1996. Voyageur Press. Stillwater, MN.

Flavored oils add interest to dipping sauces, salads, meat dishes, vegetable dishes, even *unsandwiches.* Plan to experiment with one or two recipes per week to discover the ones you like. These recipes' quantities are small to help prevent waste. Store flavored oils in glass airtight containers in the refrigerator.

Now a note about an emulsifying ingredient of which to be wary. Xanthan gum is used widely in commercially-prepared foods. This emulsifier is best avoided because it is made by fermenting corn sugar. It breaks three important prohibitions in antifungal warfare: fermentation, corn, and sugar. In fighting fungal infection it is best to avoid fermentation, which always involves fungi. Corn is a grain listed as commonly containing *aflatoxin B1,*[2] the most carcinogenic substance in the world.[3] Carefully examine labels for this sometimes-unexpected ingredient.

— — — — — — — — — — —

2. Council for Agricultural Science and Technology (CAST). Mycotoxins: risks in plant, animal, and human systems. Task Force Report No. 139. 2003. CAST. Ames, IA.

3. Cheeke, Peter R. Natural toxicants in feeds, forages, and poisonous plants. 1998. Interstate Publishers. Danville, IL.

Lemon-Thyme Olive Vegetable Dip

2 garlic cloves, peeled
½ tsp dried thyme leaves
¼ C fresh parsley
¼ tsp lemon *zest*
2 tsp lemon juice
2 tbsp *olive oil*
1¼ C water-packed *black olives*, drained

In a food processor, process garlic, thyme, and parsley until finely minced. Add the lemon zest and juice, olive oil, and the olives. Continue to process by pulsing until the olives have a rice-like texture.

Serve or refrigerate.

Makes about 2 cups

Note: Leftover amounts are good in omelets and salads.

Fresh Vegetable Dip
Go wild with dippers.

1½ C sweet onion such as Vidalia or Walla Walla, chopped
2 tbsp *butter*
1 8 oz carton *sour cream*
¼ tsp salt
¼ tsp coarsely ground black pepper
⅛ tsp ground red pepper
4 tsp snipped fresh chives

Mix together all ingredients. Chill about 1 hour. Store leftover dip in the refrigerator.

Makes about 3 cups

Use for dipping: green onions, carrots, sweet peppers, celery, cucumbers, beets, or your choice of allowed veggies.

Tomato-Basil Dip

Dehydration is a good way to store food in less space. You can do your own dehydration using your stove or machine to save the cost of the more expensive store-bought dehydrated vegetables and spices. See the *Tools* and *Sources* for information on dehydration equipment.

Beverly

½ C dried tomato pieces, chopped
8 oz *sour cream*
½ C *LifeChange Boiled Dressing* or *Homemade Mayonnaise*
1 tsp chopped fresh basil or ½ tsp dried basil
½ tsp chopped garlic
½ tsp lemon juice
¼ tsp salt
¼ tsp pepper

Soak tomato pieces in hot water until softened; drain, chop, and process in a food processor. Add remaining ingredients and process until smooth.

Cover and refrigerate for one hour or longer before serving.

Makes about 2 cups

Fresh Salsa

This fresh salsa will add zing to almost anything it is served with, from eggs to broiled or grilled meats. Don't make it more than a half hour before you serve it or it will loose its flavor and appeal. If you want the salsa really hot, leave the chili seeds in.

1 medium tomato, chopped
¼ C scallions, diced small
3 tbsp cilantro, roughly chopped
1 - 2 serrano chilies or jalapenos, chopped fine
½ tsp salt
1 tbsp fresh lime juice

Combine all ingredients in a glass or stainless steel mixing bowl.

Prepare shortly before serving. After about 3 hours, the salsa will begin to seriously deteriorate and lose flavor.

Makes about 1 cup

Roasted Garlic

You may roast the garlic ahead of time and store it well-covered in the refrigerator for up to a week. It is great in any number of recipes. Garlic and oil combinations should be refrigerated. Do not store longer than one to 14 days or prepare a fresh batch each time you need it.[4]

5 - 6 medium heads garlic
1 tbsp *olive oil*
coarse salt
fresh ground black pepper
additional *olive oil* or *butter* for spreading

Preheat the oven to 350 degrees.

Gently crush the heads of garlic to loosen but not separate the cloves. Place the garlic on aluminum foil, drizzle with the oil, and sprinkle with salt and pepper. Wrap the garlic into a tight foil package and place on a baking sheet. Roast in the oven for about 1 hour.

When cool to the touch, remove the garlic from the foil. Remove each clove from its skin: squeeze at the root end so that it pops out the top. Discard the skins. Garlic is ready to use in recipes.

Makes sufficient quantity to flavor several dishes

Serving Suggestion: Mash garlic with warm olive oil or melted butter and spread on vegetables or use in side dish.

Hint: Some kitchen supply catalogues and stores have garlic containers for baking and storing garlic.

---

4. Margen, S. and Eds. of the Univeristy of California at Berkley Wellness letter. The wellness encyclopaedia of food and nutrition. 1992. Health Letter Associates.

Bev's Bread and Butter Pickles

2 lbs small cucumbers (not miniature)
1 large onion
2 heaping tbsp coarse salt
ice cubes and water to cover
2 C unpasteurized *apple cider vinegar*
1⅓ C *honey*
¾ tsp whole mustard seeds
½ tsp celery seeds
½ tsp whole black peppercorns
½ tsp ground turmeric

Slice cucumbers and onion into ¼ inch thick rounds. Combine cucumbers, onion, and salt in a large bowl. Cover the cucumbers and onions with ice and water. Let stand for at least 3 hours. Drain, rinse well, and drain again.

Combine vinegar, honey, mustard seeds, celery seeds, pepper-corns, and turmeric in a medium saucepan. Bring to a boil. Add drained cucumber mixture and return to a boil, stirring occasionally.

Ladle pickles into clean, warmed jars. Let stand until cool. Cover. Store in the refrigerator. The pickles will stay good for a month in the refrigerator

Makes 3 pints

Oils
Useful for dipping sauces, salad dressing,
meat and vegetable dishes, and unsandwiches.

Fried Garlic and Garlic Oil

¼ C *olive oil* or *clarified butter*
2 - 3 tbsp very finely chopped garlic

Heat oil in a skillet over high heat. When hot, add garlic carefully to avoid splashing. Stir and separate the garlic in the hot
oil. When it begins to color, in about 15 to 20 **seconds**, remove
the pan from the stove and let the pan stand until the oil is room
temperature.

Scoop out the garlic, drain well in a strainer. Store the garlic
and the oil in separate airtight containers in the refrigerator.

Yield: ¼ cup oil, 2 - 3 tbsp garlic

Note: Use as an alternative flavoring in vinaigrettes and dressings.

Parsley Oil

Parsley has a variety of dietary/culinary benefits. It protects foods from contamination; it serves as a breath freshener when a sprig is chewed. Parsley is an antioxidant which contains vitamins A and C and is a source of minerals. Curly parsley is a more attractive garnish, though the flat-leaved variety is more flavorful. This close relative of the carrot can be grown as a house plant. It will grow indoors in a brightly-lit window.

One warning: pregnant women and new mothers should avoid parsley because it can bring on early labor and inhibit lactation.[5]

This recipe can serve as a vegetable dip, salad dressing addition, or flavor enhancer for meat or vegetables.

2 large bunches of flat-leaf parsley
¼ C extra-virgin *olive oil*

Prepare a medium saucepan with salted water, a mixing bowl of ice water, and some cheesecloth. Bring the salted water to a boil. Rinse the parsley and add it to the boiling water. Cook until bright green, about 20 *seconds*. Drain and place in the ice water bath to stop the cooking process.

Place the parsley into a food processor and purée, then place into a double thickness of the cheesecloth. Squeeze the juice into a small bowl.

Add the olive oil to the parsley juice. Season with salt. Store in the refrigerator in an airtight container. Can be kept for up to one week.

Makes about ½ cup

— — — — — — — — — —

5. Garrett, H. Herb of the month - parsley. Nov 2003. 6(3). 22-23. The Dirt Doctor's Dirt.

Chili Oil

½ C *coconut oil shortening* or *clarified butter*
3 tbsp dried red chili flakes

Heat oil in a wok or skillet. As soon as it starts to smoke, toss in the chili flakes ~ be careful not to splash. Remove from heat and let stand until completely cool.

Transfer oil to a clean, dry glass jar and store in a cool place. If desired, you can strain out the chilies after 2 or 3 days to store them separately or to discard.

Makes ½ C oil

Shallots and Oil

¼ C *coconut oil shortening* or *clarified butter*
1 medium shallot, sliced into thin rings (about 3 tbsp)

Heat the oil in a skillet over high heat. Add shallots to the hot oil ~ be careful not to splash. Stir and separate the shallots in the hot oil. When they begin to color, 15 to 20 **seconds**, remove from heat. Cool to room temperature.

Strain out the shallots and reserve the flavored oil. Store shallots and oil in separate airtight containers in the refrigerator.

Makes ¼ C oil

Salad Dressings

Basic Oil Dressing

⅓ C *apple cider vinegar* or lemon juice
⅔ C *olive oil*
1½ tsp salt
¼ tsp pepper
Optional: ⅛ - ¼ tsp *stevia*
        1 clove garlic, whole

Place all ingredients in a liquid-tight container and shake to mix well. Refrigerate for 2 hours.

Strain the oil and store in the refrigerator in an airtight glass container.

Makes 1 cup

Basic Vinaigrette

1 C *olive oil*
⅓ C *apple cider vinegar*
1 tsp salt
⅛ tsp pepper
2 tbsp chopped chives

Place all ingredients in a liquid-tight container and shake to mix well. Store in the refrigerator in an airtight glass container.

Makes 1½ - 2 cups

Basic French Dressing

1½ C *olive oil*
¾ C *apple cider vinegar*
¼ C *honey*
1 tbsp minced onion
1½ tsp salt
1 tsp paprika
½ tsp dry mustard
¼ tsp black pepper

Place all ingredients in a blender container; cover and process on high speed for one minute. Pour into an airtight glass container and chill. Store in the refrigerator.

Makes 2½ cups

French Dressing with Tomato

⅓ C canned stewed tomatoes
1 tbsp tomato paste
1 - 2 tbsp grated onion
1 - 2 tbsp fresh lemon juice
¼ C *apple cider vinegar*
½ C *olive oil*
1 tsp paprika
½ tsp salt
1½ tbsp *honey*

Combine stewed tomatoes and tomato paste in a blender or food processor container; purée. Add grated onion, fresh lemon juice, vinegar, olive oil, paprika, salt, and honey. Blend well.

Place in a closed container and store in the refrigerator. Shake before serving.

Makes 1 cup

Stick blender method: Combine puréed tomato mixture, grated onion, half of the lemon minus the seeds and peel, paprika, salt, and honey in a tall, slender container. Blend. Add vinegar and olive oil. Blend.

Condiments

Tangy Catsup

2½ tsp cloves
2 inch stick of cinnamon
2 tsp celery seed
2 C *apple cider vinegar*
3 12 oz cans tomato paste
1 tbsp finely grated fresh onion with its juice
¼ tsp white pepper
½ tsp cayenne
1 tsp salt
½ tsp cinnamon
½ tsp allspice
1½ tsp cloves
½ tsp dry mustard
1 tsp chili powder
1½ C *honey*

In a two quart sauce pan, combine cloves, cinnamon, celery seed, and vinegar. Bring to a boil, remove from heat, and let stand 10 minutes. Strain out the spices and return the vinegar liquid to the sauce pan.

Add remaining ingredients to the vinegar. Stir well with a wire whisk then simmer on low heat for 20 to 30 minutes.

Store in covered containers and refrigerate or freeze.

Makes 3 pints

LifeChange Boiled Dressing

This old-fashioned recipe will fit into your meal plan where you previously used mayonnaise. With the vinegar and lemon juice, it should keep in the refrigerator at least a week. A *Homemade Mayonnaise* recipe prepared without cooking follows this recipe, if you prefer.

Beverly

2 tbsp *arrowroot*
¼ tsp *stevia* or Stevia Plus
½ tsp salt
¾ tsp dry mustard
3 tbsp *apple cider vinegar*
3 tbsp lemon juice
2 tbsp *butter*
½ C *heavy cream*
⅛ tsp pepper
2 *eggs*

Pour hot water into the bottom of a *double boiler.*

In a small mixing bowl, combine all dry ingredients; set aside. In a separate bowl, combine the vinegar and lemon juice. Set aside. Place butter, cream, and pepper in a large bowl. Set aside.

In the top of a double boiler, whisk the eggs until light in color. Add the dry ingredients to the eggs and whisk until smooth. Slowly add the vinegar/lemon juice mixture. Cook over boiling water, stirring constantly, until dressing has thickened.

Remove from heat and gradually stir the hot mixture into the butter and cream. Cool and store covered in the refrigerator.

Makes about 1 cup

Homemade Mayonnaise

1 *egg*, raw, pasteurized
1 tbsp *apple cider vinegar*
½ tsp dry mustard
¼ tsp paprika
½ tsp salt
⅛ tsp cayenne pepper
1 tbsp *honey*
1 C grape seed oil
1 tbsp lemon juice

Place egg, vinegar, dry mustard, paprika, salt, cayenne, and honey in a blender container; process until smooth.

With blender on lowest speed, slowly add half the oil then the lemon juice then the remaining oil. Continue processing until oil has been distributed thoroughly for a creamy texture; scrape container sides if necessary.

Makes 2 cups

Hint: This recipe can successfully be doubled but not tripled.

Fresh Basil Mayonnaise

Delicious with raw vegetables.

1 C *Homemade Mayonnaise* or *Boiled Dressing*
¼ C snipped fresh basil leaves
several grinds of fresh pepper

In a medium mixing bowl, combine all ingredients by hand.

Keep refrigerated in an airtight container for up to a week.

Makes about 1 cup

Orange Mayonnaise

Excellent as a sauce for steamed asparagus or broccoli. Great
for dipping and as the base for chicken salad. The use of
orange zest and orange oil is permissible. The oil comes from
the zest and is almost 100 percent d-limonene, an anti-cancer
constituent.

Virginia

1 C *Homemade Mayonnaise* or *LifeChange Boiled Dressing*
2 tsp grated orange *zest*
2 - 3 drops *orange oil*
1 tsp mild curry powder, optional

In a medium glass mixing bowl, combine all ingredients and let sit
for half an hour to develop flavor. Thin with ½ teaspoon vinegar,
if desired.

Makes about 1 cup

Horseradish Cream

This is so easy to make, very delicious with roast beef. Fresh horseradish is best, but sometimes hard to find. To use bottled horseradish, first drain well and squeeze dry. Use only horseradish not stored in vinegar.

1 C *heavy cream*
1 tbsp grated horseradish, or to taste

Whip the cream until you have soft peaks. Stir in the horseradish and serve at once.

Makes about 1 cup

LifeChange Hollandaise Sauce

Care should be taken when making any Hollandaise sauce because it can easily curdle or split. Have all your ingredients and equipment together and ready before starting.

½ C *butter*, preferrably unsalted
2 tbsp *apple cider vinegar*
⅛ tsp cayenne or white pepper
2 tsp fresh lemon juice
¼ C cold water
2 large *egg* yolks
⅛ tsp salt

In a small stainless steel sauce pan, melt butter; keep butter warm throughout next steps.

In a separate stainless steel sauce pan, combine vinegar, pepper, and lemon juice. Bring to a boil and cook until reduced to half its original volume. Whisk in water and egg yolks and continue whisking to combine well. Heat over very low heat, whisking continuously at moderate speed; remove the pan from the heat occasionally to make sure you aren't cooking the yolks too quickly. When the yolk mixture clings to the wires of the whisk and you can see the bottom of pan between strokes, remove the pan from the heat and continue to stir so mixture will cool slightly and yolks will not overcook. Yolk mixture must continue to stay warm.

Gradually, in slow, thin stream, whisk the warm melted butter into the yolk mixture. Do not stop the stream until it is all incorporated, a full 3 to 4 minutes. Be sure butter and yolk mixture both stay warm during this process. If sauce becomes too thick while adding butter, whisk in a few drops of hot water. Finished sauce should be light in color, not too thick, and should evenly coat the back of a spoon. Serve immediately or keep the sauce warm by setting the sauce pan in tepid water and serve within an hour. Whisk again for a few seconds until smooth before serving.

Makes about 1 cup

Maltaise Sauce

A delicious variation of the *LifeChange Hollandaise*. Excellent on fresh steamed asparagus or to add variety to baked or grilled poultry.

1 C *LifeChange Hollandaise*
¼ C fresh orange juice *or* 4 drops *orange oil*
½ tsp fresh grated orange *zest*

Place *Hollandaise* in a medium glass or stainless steel mixing bowl. Gently whisk in orange juice or oil and zest.

Makes about 1¼ cup

Mousseline Sauce

Another flavorful variation of *LifeChange Hollandaise*. to use with meats, fish, or vegetables. The addition of horseradish is an excellent way to provide variety in your meat and fish meal plans. Try it on grilled salmon or standing rib roast.

¼ C *heavy cream*
1 C *LifeChange Hollandaise*

Whip heavy cream until stiff peaks form. Gently fold into *Hollandaise*. Serve immediately.

Makes about 1¼ cup

Variation: If desired, use ¼ cup of *Horseradish Cream* in place of the heavy cream; or add tarragon, thyme, rosemary, or other herbs or juices which will complement your meal.

Mustard

In a stainless steel, glass, or ceramic bowl (avoid aluminum) mix 8 parts mustard powder (see *Sources*) by volume with 7 parts liquid. Mustard is hot when first mixed, then mellows with age. Refrigeration nearly stops the heating process. Store at room temperature for 8 weeks for mild mustard, 6 weeks for nippy, or 4 weeks for hot before moving to the refrigerator.[6]

LifeChange Mustard

1 C dry mustard powder (4 oz dry weight)
3 oz *apple cider vinegar*
3 oz cool filtered water
½ tsp salt
1 tbsp *honey*

Mix until smooth. Pack in glass jars.

Makes about 1¾ cups

----

6. Penzeys Spices. www.penzeys.com December 2003.

Honey Mustard

4 tbsp dry mustard powder
2 tbsp water
1 tsp *apple cider vinegar*
1 tbsp grape seed oil
2 tbsp *honey*

In a stainless steel, glass, or ceramic mixing bowl, combine the mustard powder with the water and vinegar to make a stiff paste. Whisk in the oil until mixture is smooth. Whisk in the honey.

Makes about ½ cup

Variation: Omit the vinegar. Replace with 1 tbsp lemon juice and 1 tsp lemon *zest*.

Chinese Mustard

¼ C boiling water
¼ C dry English mustard
½ tsp salt
2 tsp grape seed oil

In a stainless steel, glass, or ceramic mixing bowl, stir boiling water into dry mustard. Add salt and oil.

For a yellower color, add a dash of turmeric.

Makes about ½ cup

Basic Level Fish Sauce

1 C *Boiled Dressing*
1 boiled *egg*
1 tsp dill seasoning

Or:

2 tsp *apple cider vinegar*
½ C *heavy cream*
organic seasonings, as desired

Mix ingredients together and keep refrigerated.

Makes about 1 cup

Note: The secondary list of ingredients provides an opportunity
for experimentation with many types of flavorings.

Garden Vegetable Sauce

2 C stewed tomatoes with liquid
2 tbsp tomato paste
1 tbsp chopped fresh mint **or** ½ tsp crushed dried mint
1 tsp *honey*

Combine undrained tomatoes, tomato paste, mint, and honey in a saucepan. Bring to a boil then simmer uncovered for 5 minutes.

Serve hot over summer or winter squash or eat alone as a side dish.

Makes about 2¼ cup

Aioli

Aioli is the classic French Provençal sauce. Think of it as garlic mayonnaise. Simple and rustic, it is often served with hard-cooked eggs, fish, or vegetables. Many cooks have their own versions, which range from a strong emulsion of raw garlic, salt, and oil to one enhanced with raw egg yolks, lemon juice, and mustard. The traditional tool used to make aioli is a mortar and pestle.

The recipe that follows packs a lot of punch, so use it sparingly. **It will keep a day or two in the refrigerator** and can be used to perk up dressings and cold soups or to smear on chicken before roasting. For food safety reasons, this does not have a raw egg yolk, but a pasteurized one could be added before the olive oil is added. This will make the aioli less garlicky.

4 cloves garlic
pinch of kosher, sea, or Celtic salt
1 C extra-virgin *olive oil*
1 tsp fresh lemon juice
½ tsp dry mustard
salt and freshly ground pepper to taste
½ tsp cold water

Sprinkle peeled garlic cloves with the salt and use a mortar and pestle, food processor, or the back of a fork to mash the garlic cloves into a smooth paste. Place the mixture in a bowl.

Pour the oil in a **very slow,** thin stream over the garlic mixture while you use the pestle or the back of a fork or a whisk to work the oil into the garlic. Once half of the oil is worked in, whisk in the lemon juice, mustard, salt, and pepper to taste. Slowly add and work in the remainder of the oil.

~ continued p. 137

The mixture should be slightly thinner than commercial mayonnaise. If it becomes too thick you can add a bit more water, one teaspoon at a time.

Makes about 1½ cups

Variations: Add either of the following when adding the salt
and pepper:
~ 2 tsp minced fresh rosemary, or
~ a large pinch of saffron threads and 1 tablespoon
of *honey*

Fruit Dressing

1 C plain *yogurt*
1 tsp *honey* or ¼ tsp *stevia*, powder or liquid

Mix ingredients together and refrigerate about 1 hour. Serve over fresh fruit, or as a fruit dip.

Or, if you don't have yogurt:

2 tbsp *apple cider vinegar*
1 C *heavy cream*
1 tsp *honey* or ¼ tsp *stevia,* powder or liquid

Mix together the vinegar, cream, and sweetener. Chill about 1 hour. Serve over fresh fruit.

Makes about 1¼ cups

Cream Dressing
This is another variation of the *Fruit Dressing*.

½ - 1 tbsp *honey*, to taste
3 - 4 tbsp lemon juice, to taste
1 C *heavy cream*
½ tsp salt

In a small glass or stainless bowl, combine the honey and lemon juice.

In a large mixing bowl, add salt to the heavy cream and beat until soft peaks form. Continue beating while very slowly adding the honey-lemon juice mixture. When thoroughly blended, place in a serving dish.

Serve over fruit or custard. Store in the refrigerator.

Makes 1¼ cups

Fruit Salad Dressing with Celery Seed

⅓ C *honey*
⅛ tsp (about ⅓ dropper) of *stevia* clear liquid
¼ C lemon juice
2 tsp *apple cider vinegar*
1 tsp dry mustard
½ tsp salt
½ C *olive* or sesame *oil*
1 tsp celery seed

In a blender container, combine the honey, stevia, lemon juice, vinegar, mustard, and salt. Blend until smooth. With the blender on low speed, add the oil.

Place in a liquid-tight container and stir in the celery seed. Chill.

Makes about 1 cup

Crème Fraîche

This much milder form of sour cream is delicious with berries or just about any place you'd use sour cream.

Beverly

1 C *heavy cream*
1 C *sour cream*

In a glass or stainless steel mixing bowl, combine the two creams. Let stand lightly covered for 24 hours at room temperature.

Place in a tightly sealed jar in the refrigerator. Keeps one week.

Makes 2 cups

Shallot Herb Butter

½ C (1 stick) unsalted *butter*, at room temperature, divided
2 tbsp shallots, finely chopped
1 tbsp garlic, finely chopped
1 tbsp flat-leaf parsley, finely chopped

In a small skillet over low heat, melt 1 tsp butter, then add shallots and garlic. Cook, stirring, for 3 to 4 minutes. Cool to room temperature.

In a small mixing bowl, cream the remaining butter then add the shallot mixture and the parsley. Stir well.

Store, wrapped in wax paper, for up to 1 week in the refrigerator. May freeze for up to 2 months.

Makes ½ cup

LifeChange Cranberry Sauce

12 - 16 oz bag cranberries, fresh or frozen
1 - 2 C water*
1 tbsp *orange zest* **or** ¼ tsp *orange oil*, if desired
⅓ C *honey*
½ tsp *stevia*

Pick through the cranberries and discard any black or wilted berries.

In a medium sauce pan, heat cranberries and water over medium heat. Bring to a boil and continue boiling until the cranberries have all popped, about 10 minutes. Remove from heat.

Add orange zest or oil, if desired; add honey and stevia. Stir to mix well. Pour into a serving bowl. Serve warm or cold.

Cranberry sauce will set as it cools. Store covered in the refrigerator.

Serves 4 - 8

* *Note*: Use 1 cup of water for a thicker sauce, 2 cups for thinner sauce. Adjust to desired consistency.

Berry Jams

Strong-colored berries are a rich source of cancer and disease-fighting *phytochemicals*, vitamins, minerals, and fiber.[7] Honey has its vitamins and minerals, too[8] ~ so here's a jam that's good for you. Raspberries, blueberries, loganberries (a variety of blackberries), cranberries, and strawberries all contain ellagic acid, an anticancer food constituent which does not seem to break down during cooking. This should make these cooked recipes valuable. Berries are also a good source of vitamin C and fiber.

My neighbor, Carol, remembers her mother making smaller batches of berry jams and jellies because they taste better eaten within a month or two. Frozen berries make it possible to use the bounty of summer throughout the winter. If your family eats the jam quickly, double the quantities given.

Freezing berries is simple. Cranberries and blueberries are frozen without washing. Raspberries and blackberries should be washed and drained. To freeze berries, line a cookie sheet with wax paper and spread berries in a single layer. When they have become solid, place them in a locking freezer bag and label. Most berries will stay good up to ten months when frozen. Cranberries will last up to a year frozen.[7]   *Beverly*

---

7. Joseph, J. A. Nadeau, D. Underwood, A. The color code: a
    revolutionary eating plan for optimum health. 2002. Hyperion. NY.

Using honey to make jam

~ Use light-colored *honey* that has a mild flavor.

~ Tapioca flour thickens jam made with honey and shortens the time required to make the jam. It also gives a higher yield than simple reduction.

Dilute the *tapioca flour* with a little water and add it to the jam after the jam has partially reduced.

~ Cook the jam slowly to prevent scorching. Use a heat diffuser if you have one to verify that the heat is evenly distributed.

~ Test jam with a spoon or saucer. Dip the spoon in the jam to see if the jam coats the spoon, or put some on a saucer, tilting it to cool the jam.[8]

Basic Berry Jam

2½ lbs berries, fresh or frozen, washed (*see Processes*)
juice of 1 lemon
2½ C *honey*

In a large sauce pan, cook the berries with the lemon juice until they are mushy. Add the honey and mix well. Boil hard for 20 minutes, stirring constantly.

Cool slightly. Pour into warm, sterilized jars. Add ¼ inch melted paraffin.

Makes about 2 pints

— — — — — — — — — —

8. Parkhill, J. The wonderful world of honey. 1977. Cookbook Publishers, Inc. Lenexa, KS.

Cherry Jam

14 C cherries, washed, pitted, and chopped
1½ C *honey*
½ C *tapioca flour*
2 tbsp water

Place cherries with their juice and honey in a large saucepan. Bring to a boil to reduce slightly.

Dilute tapioca flour with water and add to cherries. Cook to thicken to desired consistency; stir occasionally to mix and to keep the mixture from sticking to the bottom of the pot.

Cool slightly. Pour into warm, sterilized jars. Add ¼ inch melted paraffin.

Makes 4 - 6 pints

Raspberry or Blackberry Jam

18 C raspberries, washed
2 C *honey*
½ C *tapioca flour*
2 tbsp water

Cook berries with honey until reduced about one-third.

Dilute tapioca flour with water and add to berries. Cook to thicken to desired consistency.

Cool slightly. Pour into warm, sterilized jars. Add ¼ inch melted paraffin.

Makes 4 - 6 pints

Strawberry Jam

16 C strawberries
4 C *honey*
½ C *tapioca flour*
2 tbsp water

Mash the berries in a large cooking pot. Add the honey and cook until berries have reduced by one-third.

Dilute tapioca flour with water, stir to mix well, and add to berries. Continue simmering until reduced to desired consistency.

Cool slightly. Pour into warm, sterilized jars. Add ¼ inch melted paraffin to seal.

Makes 6 - 7 pints

Blueberry Jam

14 C blueberries, washed and stems removed
1 C *honey*
½ C *tapioca flour*
2 tbsp water

Mash the berries in a large cooking pot. Add the honey and cook until berries have reduced by one-third.

Dilute tapioca flour with water, stir to mix well, and add to berries. Continue simmering until reduced to desired consistency.

Cool slightly. Pour into warm, sterilized jars. Add ¼ inch melted paraffin to seal.

Makes 4 - 6 pints

Berry Syrup

This syrup has a very intense flavor and color. Very little
is needed on pancakes or waffles.

3 tbsp cherry or blueberry concentrate (*see Sources*)
2 tbsp *honey*
⅛ tsp liquid *stevia*

Combine all ingredients in a small container or bowl.

Store leftover syrup in an airtight container in the refrigerator.

Makes about ⅓ cup

Chapter Five

Main Dishes

The centerpiece of a family celebration or a contemplative dinner for one ~ each meal we eat contributes to our overall health and well-being. We must daily decide what the culinary focal point will be for each of those meals. It often seems difficult just to plan and prepare one more meal, much less try to make it healthy. Is it really possible to wage culinary warfare on fungal problems, enjoy a variety of entrées without exploding the budget, and still not get bogged down in constantly thinking about food? Yes!

Think outside of the box!

Planning is the key. Establish a seven to 14 day meal plan and include healthy, even unusual choices to fit that overall plan. This will encourage and enable you to try one or two new food items or ideas per week, which will help prevent waste.

Different meat choices include tuna or salmon steaks. Canned tuna should be white albacore packed in water. Drain the tuna and toss with a can of cooked, drained white beans, fresh herbs, tiny tomato halves, and your favorite vinaigrette and a *LifeChange Step-Up Level* dinner is served.

Free-range chicken breasts with the right mix of herbs and spices can turn plain into flavor-filled for exotic stir-fries and hearty entrée salads.

Eggs are useful, quickly prepared, hearty additions to main dish planning. Eggs and omelets are just the beginning. Eggs can morph into frittatas, egg and veggie *unsandwiches*, and heavenly hash suppers. Eggs combined with colorful vegetables have visual appeal and increase important vegetable intake. Fry eggs sunny side up, scramble them with butter and cream, or boil them; devil them with *LifeChange Boiled Dressing, Homemade Mayonnaise,* or *LifeChange Mustard* and add leftover meats and flavorings.

Use a newly-discovered salad to design your own "Sandwich Platters." Assemble any of your favorite sandwich fillings, substitute with allowed foods, and wrap them in lettuce leaves for a "wrap sandwich" or layer with sliced jicama, celeriac, fresh cilantro, or *Dilled Cucumbers* to eat an "open-face" style *unsandwich.* Top with toasted sesame seeds or other allowable nuts and your favorite newly-discovered dressing.

Other useful items in entrée preparations are your own ground nut meals and a carrot powder manufactured by Seagate (*see Sources*). Combine equal amounts of the nut meal and carrot powder, add seasonings of your choice (see listing), and use as "breading" to fry or bake meats. You can also add enough butter or oil to the seasoned nut meal/carrot powder mixture to make it crumbly, then sprinkle it on top of meat or vegetable casseroles or use as you would any cracker-type breading.

Meats' Seasonings

The right herbs and spices can make the difference between could-have-been and a meal to be remembered. These are suggested seasonings for different meat choices. Any combination of what you have can be used. Expand your experience with herbs slowly. Plan a meat for the menu and choose an herb new to you. Taste and imagination are your guides.

BEEF - curry, chili powder, thyme, garlic, sage, oregano, basil, dry mustard, paprika, cumin, cinnamon, allspice, coriander, turmeric, saffron, cardamom, fennel, fresh-grated horseradish

CHICKEN - paprika, thyme, sage, bay laurel, marjoram, tarragon, cilantro, cumin, lemon pepper, basil, garlic, ginger, rosemary, fennel, turmeric, saffron, mint, cloves, cinnamon, curry

FISH - dry mustard, paprika, curry, bay laurel, cayenne, chives, turmeric, saffron, thyme, lemon pepper, dill

LAMB - mint, rosemary, garlic, curry, basil, oregano, fennel, cardamom, coriander, saffron

TURKEY - sage, dill, cumin, cilantro, garlic, tarragon, thyme, fennel, saffron, cayenne, curry

VEAL - bay laurel, ginger, marjoram, curry, parsley, thyme, tarragon, garlic, turmeric, coriander

Fried-Chicken Seasoning

This is a variation on a well known restaurant's recipe for frying chicken. It can be used as a seasoning for baking or frying.

2 C *tapioca flour*
$\frac{1}{2}$ tsp salt
$\frac{1}{2}$ tsp thyme
$\frac{1}{2}$ tsp basil
$\frac{1}{2}$ tsp oregano
1 tsp ground ginger
2 tsp garlic salt
1 tbsp celery salt
1 tbsp black pepper
1 tbsp dry mustard

~~~~~

$\frac{1}{4}$ C paprika

Stir together the first 10 ingredients. Keep the paprika separate. Keep seasoning mixture and paprika in covered containers in the refrigerator.

Makes about $2\frac{1}{4}$ cups

To use: Rinse chicken pieces and dry with a paper towel. Sprinkle the dry mixture on the chicken, then sprinkle paprika on the chicken pieces. The chicken is ready for either baking or frying.

Note: We recommend you avoid vegetable oils and fry in organic lard, organic beef tallow, or *coconut oil*. These will not change into trans fatty acids when exposed to extended heating where vegetable oils do change into trans fatty acids.

Crisp Baked Lemon Chicken

zest and juice of ½ lemon
¼ C butter
1 C ground flax seed
1 tsp paprika
½ tsp seasoned salt
2 lbs chicken drumsticks (10 to 12 drumsticks)

Preheat oven to 400 degrees. Melt butter over low heat and allow to cool slightly.

Measure zest, lemon juice, and melted butter into one shallow bowl, the flax, paprika, and salt in another.

Dip the chicken pieces into the juice mixture then the dry mixture. Place the chicken pieces on a rack in a baking pan and cover loosely with aluminum foil. Bake for 40 minutes.

Remove the foil and continue baking for up to 20 minutes or until chicken is tender.

Serves 4

Lemon-Orange Rosemary Chicken

3 - 4 lb chicken, cut into 10 pieces, rinsed, and pat dry
coarse salt and freshly ground white pepper
1½ tbsp *coconut* or *olive oil*
16 small boiling onions, peeled
½ small onion, cut into ¼-inch dice
½ tsp *honey*
¾ C chicken *stock*
zest of ½ orange, finely grated
juice of ½ lemon (about 2 tbsp)
2 medium cloves garlic, very finely chopped
1½ tsp chopped fresh rosemary
¼ tsp ground cumin
⅓ C small pitted, water-packed *black olives*
1 tbsp unsalted *butter*

Season chicken with salt and pepper. Heat oil in a *Dutch oven* over medium-high heat until oil just begins to smoke. Add chicken pieces and cook until brown, 2 to 3 minutes per side. Transfer to a platter or a baking sheet.

Pour off all but 1 tablespoon of fat from Dutch oven. Reduce heat to medium. Add onions and honey, cook until onions are light golden, about 5 minutes. Add stock, orange zest, lemon juice, garlic, rosemary, cumin, and browned chicken pieces. Cover and simmer for 15 minutes.

Add olives and simmer, covered, until chicken is tender, about 10 minutes more. Remove chicken and transfer to a serving platter.

Swirl butter into the liquid left in the pan until melted. Taste and adjust for seasoning. Pour sauce over chicken.

Serves 6 - 8

Fresh Basil Roasted Chicken with Garlic Sauce

2½ - 3 lb chicken
2 tbsp unsalted *butter*, softened
¼ C chopped fresh basil
¼ C chopped fresh parsley
¼ tsp salt
⅛ tsp ground black pepper
1 C whole, fresh basil leaves or other fresh herbs, to taste
30 large cloves of garlic, unpeeled
¼ C lemon juice
2 C chicken *stock* or low-salt prepared *broth*
salt and freshly ground black pepper to taste
fresh leaves for garnish

Preheat oven to 350 degrees.

Remove fat, neck, liver, and gizzards from the body cavity, then rinse
and pat the chicken dry. Gently separate the skin from the flesh,
running your fingers from the front to the back of the chicken and
along the leg and thigh. Be careful not to rip the skin or detach it
from the bird.

In a small bowl, mix together the butter, chopped basil and parsley,
salt, and pepper. Rub half of the butter mixture under the loosened
skin, then tuck half of the whole basil leaves under the skin; be sure
to get it under the skin around the leg and thigh.

Place four of the garlic cloves into the body cavity of the chicken and
scatter the rest around the bottom of a roasting pan. Add the lemon
juice and stock to the pan. Place the chicken, breast side up, on top
of the garlic and stock.

~ *continued, p. 157*

Roast prepared chicken in the oven. Baste occasionally with the pan juices. Roast for 1 hour or until the juice from the chicken runs clear when the thickest part of the thigh is pierced. Transfer the chicken to a heated platter and tent with aluminum foil to keep warm.

Pour the pan juices, along with the whole garlic cloves, into a blender container and purée the mixture. The garlic skins will remain whole and can be discarded. Serve with the roasted chicken.

Serves 4 - 6

Oriental Chicken

A *Step-Up Level* entrée when served with brown rice.
For something extra-special, season the rice with ginger and
turmeric. For a *Basic Level* meal, serve with *Baked* or
Mashed Sweet Potatoes.

4 chicken breasts, rinsed and pat dry
1 - 2 cloves garlic, diced
1 inch of ginger root, grated
1 tsp Chinese five-spice
2 tbsp pumpkin seeds, raw
2 tbsp pine nuts, raw
paprika, to taste

Preheat oven to 350 degrees. Grease a ovenproof baking dish.

Place chicken breasts in dish. Mix remaining ingredients together
and sprinkle over the top of the chicken. Bake for about 1 hour or
until chicken is tender.

Serves 4

Basic Chicken and Broccoli Stir-Fry
Good way to make a little meat feed a larger family.

Virginia

1 tbsp *honey*
¼ C *Bragg's Liquid Aminos*
2 green onions, sliced
2 cloves garlic, minced
2 - 3 chicken breasts, cut into long bite-sized pieces
2 - 3 bunches broccoli
4 tbsp *coconut oil* or other nonhydrogenated shortening, divided

In a medium mixing bowl, combine honey, Liquid Aminos, green onions, and garlic. Place chicken pieces into mixture and coat well. Set aside and allow to soak for at least one-half hour; refrigerate if not to be used within that half hour.

Wash broccoli and cut into bite-size pieces.

Heat 3 tablespoons shortening in a wok or large skillet. When oil is hot, add chicken pieces and stir fry until tender and cooked thoroughly. Transfer chicken to a clean serving bowl; keep warm.

Add 1 tablespoon shortening to hot wok. When oil is hot, add cut up broccoli and stir fry until it has become bright green or to desired tenderness. Return chicken pieces to the wok and mix thoroughly with broccoli. Add 1 tablespoon Liquid Aminos, if desired, and mix well. Serve with slivered almonds or chopped cashews.

Serves 4

Step-Up Level serving suggestion: serve over steamed brown rice.

Variations: Use your choice of meats and vegetables, either fresh or left over. Some considerations are water chestnuts, bamboo shoots, julienne carrots or squash. Also use Chinese five-spice, ginger, cilantro, or other Chinese spice, as desired.

Honey-Mustard Fried Chicken

¼ C *apple cider vinegar*
¼ C grape seed ˙or *olive oil*
½ C **Honey Mustard**
1 tsp fresh tarragon, chopped
1½ tsp salt, divided
½ tsp freshly ground black pepper
1 fryer-size chicken, rinsed, dried, and cut into 8 pieces
1 C *tapioca flour*
¼ C *arrowroot*
½ C *coconut oil shortening* or *clarified butter*

In a large glass or ceramic mixing bowl, prepare the marinade: blend together the vinegar, oil, **Mustard**, tarragon, 1 tsp salt, and pepper. Add the chicken pieces one at a time and turn to thoroughly coat each piece. Tightly cover with plastic wrap and marinate for 2 to 3 hours or overnight in the refrigerator.

Remove the chicken pieces from the marinade and let them drain briefly. Discard marinade. Combine the tapioca flour, arrowroot, and ½ tsp salt in a shallow dish. Roll each chicken piece in the flour mixture to coat and place on a baking sheet. Let rest for 30 minutes.

Preheat oven to 350 degrees. In a large, heavy skillet, heat the oil. Brown the chicken pieces in the hot oil a few pieces at a time until well browned, about 6 to 8 minutes each. When each piece is browned, return it to the baking sheet.

Bake the chicken pieces in the oven for 30 to 40 minutes until the juices run clear when a thicker piece is pierced.

Briefly drain the pieces on paper towels. Serve with a fresh spinach salad.

Serves 3 - 4

Chicken with Grapefruit and Tarragon

2 tbsp *coconut oil shortening* or *clarified butter*
1 fryer-size chicken, rinsed, dried, and cut into serving pieces
pinch of tarragon
2 C sliced carrots
1 medium onion, sliced
1 C celery, diagonally sliced
2 tsp *zest* of grapefruit
$\frac{1}{2}$ C fresh squeezed grapefruit juice
pinch of tarragon
$\frac{1}{4}$ tsp salt
$\frac{1}{8}$ tsp pepper
1 tbsp *arrowroot*
$\frac{1}{4}$ C cold water
1 grapefruit, peeled, sectioned, and drained

Preheat a 10 inch skillet. Add oil or butter. Sprinkle tarragon on the chicken pieces and place in skillet until lightly browned.

Pour off most of the fat. To the skillet, add carrots, onion, celery, grapefruit zest and juice, tarragon, salt, and pepper. Cover and cook on low heat until meat is tender, about 45 minutes.

Place meat and vegetables on a platter and keep warm.

Blend arrowroot with water and add to pan drippings to make a sauce. Cook stirring until thickened. Add grapefruit sections and heat. Serve the sauce over the chicken and vegetables.

Serves 4 - 6

Chicken Gumbo

Stew becomes gumbo with the addition of okra.

4 lb roasting chicken, cut into pieces
3 slices of crisp *bacon*
1½ C sliced onion
5 C liquid (add water to *stock* to make the full amount)
½ C chopped celery
2 tsp salt
1 lb or 3 tomatoes, peeled and quartered
1 *celeriac* (*celery root*), peeled and cubed
4 spears asparagus, sliced crosswise
¼ C chopped red sweet peppers
½ lb fresh okra, sliced crosswise
2 tbsp *arrowroot* powder
¼ C warm water

Rinse chicken pieces, drain, and pat dry.

In a 6 quart *Dutch oven,* sauté bacon then onions until golden. Remove to a bowl with slotted spoon.

Sauté chicken in the same pan until lightly brown. Add bacon-onion mixture, stock, celery, and salt. Bring to a boil, cover, reduce heat, and simmer for 30 minutes.

Skim off excess fat. Add tomatoes, celeriac, asparagus, and peppers. Bring to a boil and simmer, covered, for 15 minutes. Add okra and simmer, covered, for an additional 10 minutes or until all ingredients are fork tender.

Add arrowroot to warm water and stir into stew to thicken slightly.

Serves 4 - 6

Step-Up Level Variation: Add 1 C baby lima beans when adding tomatoes.

Grilled Tuna Niçoise

¼ C *olive oil*, divided
1 tbsp canned anchovies, mashed
1 clove garlic, mashed
2 small tomatoes (about ¾ lb), seeded and diced
¼ C chopped, pitted water-pack *black olives*
3 tbsp water-packed/ non-fermented *capers*, drained and rinsed
2 tbsp chopped fresh basil
1 tbsp chopped fresh thyme
½ tsp pepper
4 1-inch thick tuna steaks (1¼ lbs total)
½ tsp salt
fresh thyme sprigs, for garnish

Preheat a charcoal grill, gas grill, or oven broiler on high heat.

In a medium mixing bowl, blend 2 tablespoons olive oil, mashed anchovy, and garlic. Add tomatoes, olives, capers, basil, thyme, and pepper. Mix well, set aside.

Rinse tuna steaks and pat dry. Brush with remaining 2 tablespoons olive oil and sprinkle with salt.

Grill or broil tuna for 3 minutes on each side for medium-rare or until cooked as desired. Place on serving plates. Spoon tomato mixture over tuna and garnish with fresh thyme.

Serves 4

Variation: Substitute chicken breasts or pork chops. Both will do well with this zesty tomato-garlic topping.

Wrapped Fish Steaks

1 lb fish steaks
zest and juice of half a lemon
salt
paprika to taste
1 tbsp *butter*

Preheat oven to 450 degrees.

Place fish on rectangle of heavy aluminum foil. Sprinkle with lemon peel, lemon juice, salt, and paprika. Dot with butter. Wrap securely and place on baking sheet.

Bake for 10 to 13 minutes or until fish flakes easily.

Serves 3 - 4

LifeChange Italian Sausage Spaghetti

1 spaghetti squash
6 6"- 8" organic *Italian sausages*
¼ C extra-virgin *olive oil*
¾ C onion, chopped
1½ C beef or chicken *stock* or broth
2 23 oz cans tomatoes, hand crushed
salt, to taste
6 fresh basil leaves, torn into small pieces
1 pinch dried oregano
salt and freshly-ground black pepper, to taste

Preheat oven to 400 degrees. Pierce the skin of the squash several times. Place the whole squash in an oven-proof pan and add enough water to cover the bottom of the pan. Place in oven to bake for about 1 hour or until skin is easily pierced with a fork.

Remove the casings from the sausages, break meat up into chunks, and set aside.

Heat olive oil in a large skillet over medium heat. Add onion and cook until translucent, about 3 minutes. Stir in the sausage and cook until lightly browned, about 5 minutes. Drain off excess fat. Add stock or broth and stir to combine. Raise heat and boil until liquid has reduced slightly, about 3 additional minutes.

Add tomatoes, salt, and return to a boil, then lower heat and simmer, uncovered, until the sauce has thickened slightly, about 20 minutes. Stir in basil, oregano, and pepper; add additional salt and pepper to taste.

Cut the cooled squash in half, remove the seeds, and scrape the flesh out with a fork. It will look like spaghetti noodles. Place squash on serving platter and top with sausage-tomato sauce.

Serves 4

Roast Boneless Leg of Lamb Rolled with Mint Pesto

The mint sauce is rolled inside this boned leg of lamb so that it bastes the meat during baking.

5 lb boned leg of lamb
1½ C packed mint leaves
4 cloves garlic, peeled
2 tbsp fresh lemon juice
½ C pine nuts
¼ C plus 2 tbsp *olive oil*, divided
salt
freshly ground black pepper

Preheat oven to 375 degrees.

In a roasting pan, spread boned lamb flat with inside facing up.

To prepare the pesto, process the mint, garlic, lemon juice, and pine nuts in a food processor until finely chopped. With the machine running, slowly add ¼ cup of the olive oil.

Spread pesto over inside of lamb. Roll or fold the lamb to enclose the filling. To help hold pesto in place, tuck in the edges of the meat. Tie a long piece of cotton string around the rolled roast. Rub remaining 2 tablespoons olive oil on the roast and sprinkle with salt and freshly ground pepper.

Roast prepared lamb for about 1½ hours until meat thermometer registers 160 degrees. Transfer the meat to a carving board and let it rest 20 minutes. Remove and discard string. Cut lamb into slices and serve.

Serves 8

Lamb Stew

A make-the-day-ahead dish. Add one 10 ounce package of peas to make it an *Step*Up *Level* Recipe.

4 tbsp *arrowroot* powder
2 tsp salt
¼ tsp pepper
2½ lbs boneless lamb, cubed
¼ C butter
1 lb boiling onions, peeled
1 bay leaf
1 tsp thyme
2 C water
1 C tomato juice
5 - 6 carrots, scrubbed
1 *celeriac (celery root),* washed, peeled, and cubed
3 tbsp fresh snipped dill

In a medium mixing bowl, combine arrowroot, salt, and pepper. Roll the cubes of lamb in the mixture to evenly coat. Reserve any remaining arrowroot mixture.

In a 5 or 6 quart *Dutch oven*, melt butter and brown the coated meat, turning as needed. Remove cubes as each becomes browned. Add more butter if needed.

Add onions to drippings in the Dutch oven. Cover and cook about 5 minutes until lightly browned. Return cooked meat to Dutch oven and add the bay leaf and thyme. Toss to coat evenly. Add water and tomato juice, stir.

Bring to a boil, reduce heat, cover, and simmer 30 minutes. Remove from heat, cool. Cover and refrigerate overnight.

~ continued, p. 168

The next day, 1½ hours before serving, place the Dutch oven over low heat and bring the stew slowly back to a boil. Add carrots and celery root, stir. Simmer for about 45 minutes until vegetables are fork tender.

Remove from heat and skim off the fat. Stir reserved arrowroot mixture into a quarter cup of water; stir until smooth, then add to stew. Remove the bay leaf and add the dill. Stir well.

Simmer, covered, 10 to 15 minutes until the liquid is slightly thickened. Remove from heat. Let stand about 5 minutes. Serve.

Serves 4 - 6

Step•Up Level Variation: Add one 10 oz. package of frozen peas during the final 15 minutes of cooking time. Simmer until peas are tender.

Lazy Day Stew

1½ pounds stew meat, cut into 1 inch cubes
1 medium onion, chopped
3 carrots, cut into ½ inch pieces
2 ribs celery, cut into ½ inch pieces
2 C cubed butternut squash
2 14.5 oz. cans stewed tomatoes, with liquid
1 tbsp dried parsley flakes
1 tsp thyme
salt and pepper, to taste
1½ tbsp quick-cooking tapioca

Preheat oven to 325 degrees or use a slow cooker set to high.

Combine all ingredients in the order listed into the crock of a slow cooker or a large oven-proof casserole dish. Cook for 5 full hours. After 2 to 3 hours, stir several times.

Serves 4

Variation: Doubles or triples quite well, if you have a large enough pot!

Sirloin Steaks with Fresh Herbs

Roasted Tomatoes:
8 plum tomatoes, halved lengthwise
salt
ground black pepper

Garnish:
½ C chopped shallots
2 tsp *olive oil*

Herb-Seasoned Steaks:
4 cloves garlic, minced
5 basil leaves, finely chopped
2 tsp chopped fresh rosemary leaves
2 tsp chopped fresh thyme leaves

pinch of salt
pinch of ground black pepper
4 6 oz sirloin steaks
2 tsp *olive oil*

Slow-Roasted Tomatoes:
Preheat oven to 225 degrees F. Sprinkle the tomatoes very lightly with the salt and pepper. Place, cut side down, on a nonstick baking sheet. Place in the oven and allow to slow roast for 6 to 7 hours. Remove from the oven and set aside.

Herb-Seasoned Steaks:
In a small bowl, combine the garlic, basil, rosemary, thyme, salt, and pepper. Brush both sides of each steak with the oil and sprinkle each side with the herb mixture. Place the steaks on a platter, cover with plastic wrap, and refrigerate for at least 2 hours.

Cook the steaks on a hot grill for 3 to 4 minutes per side for medium-rare or until they reach desired degree of doneness.

Garnish:
In a nonstick skillet over medium heat, sauté the shallots in the oil for 2 to 3 minutes or until lightly browned.

To Assemble:
Rewarm the tomatoes, if needed. Place each steak on a serving plate and top with equal amounts of shallots and tomatoes.

Makes 4 servings

Gingery Beef and Broccoli Meatballs

1 10-ounce package frozen broccoli spears
2 tbsp dehydrated onion flakes
2 tbsp fresh ginger *or* 1 ½ tsp ground ginger
4 tbsp *Bragg's Liquid Aminos*
1 tbsp lemon juice
1 lb ground beef

Preheat oven to 350 degrees. Set a meat rack inside a shallow baking pan.

Cook broccoli according to package directions but only for half the specified time. Drain and cool. Cut florets from the stems and chop the stems. Reserve florets.

In a blender container, combine chopped broccoli stems, onion flakes, ginger, Liquid Aminos, and lemon juice. Process at medium speed for 3 minutes or until mixture is puréed. Pour into a large glass mixing bowl. Add ground beef and mix thoroughly.

Cut florets into small pieces and add to the beef mixture; mix well. Shape meat mixture into 12 balls, each about 1 inch in diameter. Place on rack in pan.

Bake for 30 minutes or until cooked throughout.

Serves 2

Shredded Beef in a Bowl

A great use for leftover meat of any kind.

2 medium to large acorn squash
salt
3 C leftover roast beef
1 tbsp *olive oil*
½ medium yellow onion, chopped
4 tbsp (½ stick) *butter*
1 C *heavy cream*
1 clove garlic, minced
1 tbsp cream cheese
1 small carton plain goat-milk *yogurt or* plain regular *yogurt*
½ tsp salt
⅛ tsp pepper

Preheat oven to 350 degrees.

Cut squash in half and remove seeds. Place squash in a flat baking dish; if needed, cut off a thin slice to enable each half to sit flat. Sprinkle with salt and bake, uncovered, until the inside is tender when pierced with a fork, about 45 to 50 minutes.

While squash is baking, use two forks to shred the roast. In a large, heavy sauce pan, sautée the onion in olive oil until translucent. Add the butter to melt then gently pour in the cream, stirring constantly. Stir in the garlic and cream cheese. Simmer, stirring, until all is melted and well mixed. Stir in the yogurt, salt, and pepper and simmer on very low heat for 10 to 15 minutes to thicken, stirring occasionally to prevent sticking or scorching. Add shredded beef and heat through, continuing to stir occasionally.

When squash is tender, place each on an individual serving plate. Spoon shredded beef into each squash to fill the cavity. Serve with a fresh spinach and tomato salad.

Serves 4

Round Steak Roll-Up

1 carrot
1 zucchini squash
1 small butternut squash or half an eggplant, peeled
1 medium onion
3 - 4 pound round steak
salt and pepper, to taste
herbs and spices, to taste (parsley, cumin, garlic, sage, curry, etc.)
3 - 4 18 inch pieces of string
1 16 oz can stewed tomatoes, diced, with juice

Preheat oven to 350 degrees.

Cut carrot and squashes into thin vertical slices. Cut onion into half-rings.

Lay the round steak in a 13 x 9 oven-proof dish. Layer vegetables down the vertical center (long-ways) of the steak. Sprinkle with salt, pepper, and herbs/spices. Start with the long edge of the round steak furthest from you and roll up the meat, capturing the vegetables in the middle of the roll. Use the string to tie the roll in several places so that it holds together. Top the round steak roll with diced stewed tomatoes and their juice.

Bake for 1 hour or until tender. Add additional water or other vegetable juice to keep the steak and pan from drying out.

Transfer round steak to serving platter. Slice across the roll and tip the pieces to reveal the vegetables inside. Serve with the pan juices.

Serves 4 - 6

Tomato and Red Bean Chili

2 tbsp *coconut oil shortening*
2 lbs ground beef
1 large onion, diced
4 cloves garlic, minced
$\frac{1}{4}$ green pepper, diced
$\frac{1}{2}$ tsp black pepper
2 tsp dry sweet basil
1 tsp oregano
$\frac{1}{4}$ tsp chipotle chili pepper
1 tsp dry mustard
1 tsp salt
2 14 oz cans diced tomatoes

Preheat a large non-aluminum pot. Add the coconut oil. Add meat and brown thoroughly.

Add onion, garlic, and green pepper and cook until onions are translucent. Add spices, mix well then add tomatoes. Let simmer for 15 to 20 minutes or longer to allow the flavors to mingle.

Serves 6

Step-Up Level Variation: Add one 14 oz can of red kidney or black beans, drained, when adding the tomatoes.

Sloppy Joes

For *Step-Up Level* meal, spoon over any cooked, allowed grain.

3 lb ground meat, any allowed type ~ beef, turkey, venison
1 large onion, diced
1 green pepper, diced
1 tbsp *honey*
½ tsp *stevia*
1½ tsp dry mustard
1 tsp salt
1½ tsp pepper
1 tsp chili pepper
3 6 oz cans tomato paste

In a large, heavy skillet, brown the ground meat. Add onion and green pepper and cook until onions are translucent. Add the honey and stevia, then the seasonings and tomato paste; stir well after each addition.

Simmer long enough to allow flavors to mingle or place in the crock of a large slow cooker and simmer for several hours.

Serve over a bed of lettuce, other greens, or cooked spaghetti squash. Or serve in a bowl with *Crispy Flatbread* or *Popover Gems*.

Serves 6 - 8

Vegetable Stew

1 medium red pepper, cut in ½ inch slices
1 medium green pepper, cut in ½ inch slices
2 C onions, sliced
2 cloves garlic, crushed
4 tbsp *olive oil*, divided
2 medium zucchini, sliced
1 yellow squash, sliced
1 medium eggplant, quartered, then sliced crosswise
5 medium tomatoes, about 1½ lbs, cut into wedges
¾ tsp salt
¼ tsp pepper
1 tbsp chopped parsley

In a 12 inch skillet, sauté peppers, onions, and garlic in 1 tablespoon olive oil for about 5 minutes. Remove with slotted spoon to a large mixing bowl.

Add 1 tablespoon oil to the skillet and sauté both types of squash. Turn to cook evenly until tender, about 10 minutes. Remove with a slotted spoon and add to the sautéed peppers and onions.

Add remaining 2 tablespoons of oil to skillet and sauté the eggplant. Turn to cook evenly until tender, about 5 minutes. Transfer eggplant to the bowl with the other vegetables and lightly toss vegetables to combine.

Add tomato wedges to the skillet. Sprinkle with half each of the salt, pepper, and parsley. Top with the vegetable mixture. Add the rest of the salt, pepper, and parsley.

Simmer over low heat for at least 5 minutes, covered. Baste with the juices. Cook uncovered 2 minutes, basting, until liquid reduces to desired consistency. Serve hot.

Serves 4

Omelet 101

Tips for making the perfect omelet.

1. Use *clarified butter*, which does not burn as quickly as salted or unsalted butter. If you do use regular butter, watch it carefully to keep it from burning.

2. Whisk the eggs immediately before you pour them into the hot skillet, otherwise they will deflate. Incorporate lots of air into the eggs to ensure a light and fluffy omelet.

3. Make sure the skillet is the right temperature; hold your palm a few inches above the inside bottom of the pan. When your hand feels warm, the pan is ready.

4. After adding the eggs to the pan, simultaneously whisk the eggs and shake the skillet vigorously back and forth over the heat for about 1 minute. Keep the eggs moving to incorporate some of the runny parts with the cooked curds. The key to a fluffy omelet with a smooth surface is to stop whisking before the egg sets.

5. Use a heat-safe rubber spatula to gently fold half the omelet over a filling. Press down lightly on the half-moon to set the omelet.

6. To serve, lift the skillet with one hand and hold a serving plate in the other. Tilt the skillet to slide the curved edge of the omelet onto the plate.

About Frittatas

A frittata is a round Italian omelet that has its fillings mixed into the eggs before cooking rather than folded inside like the French omelet. Fillings can be cooked meats, sautéed vegetables, cream cheese, or leftovers. The eggs are cooked slowly over low heat and finished in the oven or under the broiler to set and lightly brown the top. The result is a firm and fluffy egg pie that can be eaten warm or at room temperature.

Scramble Omelet

A very substantial breakfast. Vary ingredients to suit your imagination and to get a good vegetable start for the day.

Chop any combination of the following: onions, leeks, green onions, asparagus, or roasted sweet peppers- red, green or yellow. Add greens: spinach, beet greens, etc.

Sauté or soften the chopped vegetables in a skillet in *butter* or *olive oil*. When vegetables are soft or translucent, add cut greens and cook briefly to heat through.

Add 1 to 2 eggs per person. Cook until eggs are set. Salt and pepper to taste.

Optional additions: *heavy cream*, ground *flax seed*, sesame seeds, or sautéed meats (*bacon*, turkey breakfast sausage, etc.).

Festive Baked Eggs

4 - 5 green onions, chopped
¼ C onion, diced
4 C fresh spinach, chopped
¼ C red bell pepper, diced
1 C *ham,* cubed
9 *eggs*
½ tsp pepper
¾ C *heavy cream*
1 tsp crushed red pepper

Preheat oven to 350 degrees.

Sauté the green onion, onion, spinach, and bell pepper. Add cubed ham and heat through.

Beat together the eggs, pepper, cream, and crushed red pepper.

Add sautéed mixture to the eggs. Pour into a greased 9 x 13 inch pan. Bake for 25 minutes.

Reduce oven to 325 degrees and bake for an additional 20 minutes. The eggs are done when a toothpick inserted in the center comes out clean.

Serves 6 - 8

Garden Frittata

8 large *eggs*
7 fresh sage leaves, thinly shredded
½ tsp coarse salt
½ tsp freshly ground pepper
1 tbsp extra-virgin *olive oil*
6 medium scallions, trimmed and thinly sliced crosswise
20 very small cherry tomatoes, halved

Beat eggs lightly with a fork. Stir in sage, salt, and pepper.

In a medium nonstick skillet with an oven proof handle, heat oil over medium heat. Add scallions but reserve 1 tablespoon of green ends. Cook, stirring occasionally, until limp, about 2 minutes.

Add eggs. Lower heat to medium-low and cook for 3 minutes, drawing eggs away from the side of the pan with a wooden spoon so that the uncooked portion runs to the side. Spread tomatoes evenly across the top and continue to cook until eggs begin to set and thicken but the surface is still runny, about 2 to 3 minutes more. Sprinkle with reserved tablespoon of scallions.

Place under a broiler until the top is set and golden brown, 1 to 1½ minutes. Remove from broiler. Serve warm or at room temperature from the pan or carefully slide onto a serving platter.

Serves 4

Dinner Frittata

8 *eggs*, beaten
salt, to taste
pepper, to taste
butter or *olive oil*
crisp *bacon*, to taste

Vegetable Choices:
1½ C or 1 lb asparagus, cut into bite-size pieces
1 lb broccoli, cut into bite-size pieces
1½ lb eggplant, peeled and diced
⅔ C green pepper, chopped
1 C onion, chopped
2 cloves garlic, chopped
2 tsp dried oregano
1½ C tomatoes, coarsely chopped

Beat eggs lightly with a fork. Stir in salt and pepper to taste.

Heat a small amount of butter or olive oil in a medium skillet. Sauté chosen vegetables until translucent or *al denté*. Remove from the skillet.

Add beaten eggs to skillet, cook for about 3 minutes. Add sautéed vegetables. Continue cooking until eggs begin to set but surface is still runny.

Place under broiler until the top is set and golden brown, about 1 to 1½ minutes. Place bacon on the top to serve.

Serves 3 - 4

Chapter Six

Breads

The treatment of breads is a major difference of the *LifeChange* eating lifestyle. These significant changes are due, in large part, to the harvesting and storage practices related to grains. The way in which most grains are stored actively promotes fungal growth. Add in their high carbohydrate content and that equals no grains allowed in the *Basic Level* of this diet. As you progress through the *Basic* into the *Step-Up Level*, some specific whole grains will be carefully added back into the diet.

Since the majority of the meals you enjoy should be from the vegetable, fruit, and protein food groups, it is common to want the comfort of foods from the "bread" group. We have found ways to utilize a few of the allowed foods to add some of these "comfort foods" back into our meal plan.

Tapioca flour comes from the yucca root, as discussed in *Vegetables*. Saponin is the antifungal element of interest in tapioca. It is also found in other plants of economic importance such as tomatoes, onions, asparagus, spinach, cucumbers, eggplants, oats, beans, and sweet potatoes. Saponins are also found in common herbs such as licorice, nutmeg, and ginseng. A major source of saponins, however, is the root of the yucca plant which is native to the southwestern United States and Mexico.

Saponins have potential as both medications and as dietary additives for use in lowering cholesterol levels in humans.[1] Information from the field of microbiology shows that sterols, from

––––––––––––

1.   Cheeke, Peter R. Natural toxicants in feeds, forages and poisonous plants. 1998. Interstate Publishers , Inc. Danville, IL.

which cholesterol is made, are probably produced by all fungi.[2] Combine these two facts and it is obvious why yucca and tapioca should be included in an antifungal diet.

Arrowroot or *tapioca flour* can be used in small amounts as substitutes for other flours in small bread-type recipes and as thickening agents (*see 1-2-3 Crepes*). Experiment with the addition or substitution of *flax meal* in your favorite recipes.

Nut flours finely-ground from allowed nuts can often be a useful substitute for other kinds of flour. Nut flours can be purchased where health foods are sold, or you can make your own nut flour with a coffee grinder (set aside for only this purpose) or a strong food processor. Nut flour can basically be substituted for other flours in your favorite recipe, but you must omit or reduce the amount of oil or fat in the recipe. The consistency of the recipes will definitely be heavy, but the taste is good and distinctive to the kind of nut flour you use. Adjust your expectations accordingly and don't be afraid to experiment. See www.foodsubs.com/Nutmeals.html for additional information on nut meals and flours.

For many bakers using this diet, the double-acting baking powder purchased off the grocery store shelf can go well beyond its "use by" freshness date before we even begin to use most of the can. Making your own fresh, single-acting baking powder not only avoids the problem of the product aging but is also thought to actually produce a finer finished baked good[3] (see *Processes*). It is important to remember that with single-acting baking powder you must mix in the liquid ingredients immediately prior to placing the recipe in the oven because the leavening action takes place when the liquid ingredients are added to the recipe. The recipe must be placed in the oven quickly before it goes flat.[3]

———————————

2.   Moore-Landecker, E. Fundamentals of the fungi. 1990. Prentice Hall. Englewood Cliffs, NJ.

3.   www.users.rcn.com/sue.interport/food/bakgsoda.html   December 2003.

1-2-3 Crepes

Crepes could be served with wilted spinach, scrambled eggs, or any other topping limited only by your imagination. For breakfast crepes, I like to make a *Fruit Rave* using 2 Granny Smith apples and frozen unsweetened cherries to spoon over my crepes.   *Beverly*

Individual recipe
1 *egg*
2 tbsp *heavy cream*
3 tbsp *tapioca flour*
pinch of salt
¼ tsp vanilla

Heat crepe pan or small, thin skillet or griddle.

Beat egg, gently add cream. Whisk in tapioca flour and salt and beat well. Add vanilla.

Pour ¼ cup batter onto center of griddle and rotate to spread thin layer across bottom of pan. Watch carefully and turn when first side is lightly browned. When second side is lightly browned, turn out onto warmed plate.

Serve with butter, stevia-sweetened yogurt, *Berry Syrup*, or a small amount of honey and fresh berries of your choice.

Makes 2 - 3 medium crepes

Larger proportions
2 *eggs*
⅓ C *heavy cream*
½ + C *tapioca flour*
½ tsp salt
½ tsp vanilla

Makes 4 - 6 medium crepes

Blueberry Pancakes

1 *egg*, beaten
¾ C almond milk, unsweetened (see *Processes*)
1 C almond flour
½ tsp baking soda
½ tsp salt
1 tsp baking powder
½ - 1 tsp cinnamon
3 tbsp *arrowroot*, divided
1 tsp vanilla
1 C blueberries

Heat griddle or large skillet; grease with *non-stick spray* or *butter*.

Blend the egg with the almond milk. In a separate bowl, combine the almond flour, baking soda, salt, baking powder, cinnamon, and 2 tablespoons arrowroot; blend well. Add to the egg mixture, then stir in the vanilla. Dust the blueberries with the remaining tablespoon of arrowroot; be sure they are covered, then fold into the batter.

Drop onto hot, greased griddle. Let the first side cook well before flipping to cook second side.

Serve simply with butter or with your choice of stevia-sweetened yogurt, *Fruit Rave, Berry Syrup*, or berries.

Makes about 8 pancakes

Fluffy Pancakes

I was so surprised at how light and fluffy these were, with the texture of a traditional pancake. *Beverly*

2 *eggs*
¼ C *heavy cream*
1 tsp vanilla
⅓ C *tapioca flour*
1 tsp baking powder
1 tsp *wheat gluten**

Heat a griddle or small skillet; grease with *non-stick spray*.

Mix the eggs, cream, and vanilla. Whisk in the dry ingredients.

Drop by ¼ cup onto hot griddle. Cook first side on medium heat until dry across the top then flip to briefly finish second side.

Serve with stevia or honey-sweetened yogurt, fruit, or *Berry Jam*.

Makes about 4 pancakes

Note: This recipe also makes great waffles. Experiment with *Step*Up Level* grains.

---

* Not for persons allergic to gluten. Substitute *arrowroot*.

Walnut Pancakes

I have also used this recipe to make waffles, with excellent results.   *Virginia*

1 C almond milk, unsweetened
2 *eggs*
1 tsp *apple cider vinega*r
1½ C walnut or other allowed nut flour
1 tsp baking powder
½ tsp salt
½ tsp soda
½ tsp *arrowroot*
1 tbsp *tapioca flour*
1 tsp vanilla
½ tsp cinnamon
2 heaping tbsp ground *flax seed*
1 tbsp *psyllium*

Heat griddle or large skillet; grease with *non-stick spray* or *butter*.

Mix together almond milk, eggs, and vinegar. Add remaining ingredients in the order listed, stir only until well blended.

Pour about ¼ cup of mixture on hot, greased griddle. Let the first side cook thoroughly before flipping to cook second side.

Serve with stevia-sweetened yogurt, mix in berries to suit, or use *Berry Syrup* or *Fruit Rave* as a substitute for syrup. Pancakes are delicious simply topped with butter or whipped heavy cream sweetened with stevia and vanilla.

Makes about 8 pancakes

Pecan Waffles

1 *egg*, lightly beaten
½ C almond milk, unsweetened
½ C *yogurt*
1 C pecan or other allowable nut flour
2 tbsp *tapioca flour*
½ tsp cinnamon
½ tsp ground coriander
1 tsp baking powder
½ tsp baking soda
½ tsp salt

Heat waffle iron as directed.

Blend together egg, almond milk, and yogurt. Add dry ingredients. Stir just until dry ingredients are wet but well mixed.

Cook on hot, greased waffle iron according to manufacturer's specifications.

Makes about 6 - 8 small waffles

Basic Tapioca Drop Biscuits

My teenage son calls these "lembas bread," the elven food
in *Lord of the Rings*, because they are golden in color,
sweet in taste, and quite filling.

1 C *tapioca flour*
6 tsp baking powder
⅛ tsp salt
1 C *heavy cream*

Preheat oven to 425 degrees. Spray a baking sheet with *non-stick
spray*.

In a medium mixing bowl, gently sift together the tapioca flour,
baking powder, and salt until thoroughly blended. Stir in the cream
and continue to stir until cream is completely absorbed; the mixture
will be sticky and somewhat crumbly.

Drop by the teaspoonful onto prepared baking sheet - mixture may
require pressing together to stay formed but will hold together quite
well during baking. Biscuits should be no more than 2 inches in
diameter to facilitate thorough baking.

Bake for 30 minutes or until the crust is golden brown and the
biscuits spring back to shape when pressed.

Makes 15 medium or 18 small biscuits

Notes and Variations:
　　　　　~ mixture doubles quite well
　　　　　~ bake thoroughly or will be very chewy in the center
　　　　　~ experiment with rosemary, thyme, cinnamon, or ginger to
　　　　　　　　go with your meal; or try adding almond flour, flax
　　　　　　　　seed, or stevia
　　　　　~ for dumplings: drop onto top of *Hearty Beef Soup* or
　　　　　　　　Chicken Gumbo then bake til done

Blueberry Muffins

This actually bakes and looks like a traditional muffin; however, it is a heavy muffin. A little is a lot!   *Virginia*

2 *eggs*, beaten
½ C ground *flax seed*
½ C *almond flour*
½ tsp soda
½ tsp salt
1 tsp baking powder
1 tsp vanilla
2 tsp *stevia* powder or extract
½ C seltzer water or sparkling mineral water
½ C blueberries

Preheat oven to 375 degrees. Grease muffin cups.

Mix all ingredients in order; reserve blueberries until after the batter is thoroughly moistened.

Spoon a scant ¼ cup into each of the greased muffin cups. Bake for 20 minutes.

Makes 6 - 8 muffins

Serve with *Berry Jam*, *Fruit Rave*, or with stevia-sweetened yogurt.

Blueberry Oatmeal Muffins

This is one of the best blueberry muffin recipes ~ and I adapted it for the *Step**Up Level. It maintains the original flavor and holds together quite well.   *Virginia*

1 *egg* or 2 *egg* whites, slightly beaten
1 C *yogurt*, plain
¼ C *butter*, softened, or a light oil may be substituted
¾ C oat flour
¾ C *tapioca flour*
1 C quick oats
⅓ C *honey*
½ tsp *stevia*
2 tsp baking powder
1 tsp cinnamon
½ tsp baking soda
¼ tsp nutmeg
¼ tsp salt (optional)
1 C fresh or frozen blueberries

Preheat oven to 375 degrees.

Line 12 medium muffin cups with paper baking cups or grease cups.

Mix all ingredients except blueberries just until flour is moistened. Batter will be lumpy. Fold in the blueberries.

Bake 20 to 25 minutes. Immediately remove from pan.

Makes about 12 muffins

Crispy Flatbread

This uses the same ingredients as *Fluffy Pancakes*, but it toasts into a cracker-like bread. Great with soups.

Beverly

2 *eggs*
¼ C *heavy cream*
1 tsp vanilla
⅓ C *tapioca flour*
1 tsp baking powder
1 tsp wheat *gluten**

Preheat oven to 250 to 300 degrees. Prepare griddle with *non-stick spray* and heat.

Mix the eggs, cream, and vanilla. Add the dry ingredients. Mix lightly.

Pour ¼ cup of batter onto a preheated griddle. Move the griddle around to distribute the batter very thinly. Turn when batter bubbles.

Place pancakes in a single layer on a wire rack or vented-style pizza pan. Place the rack or pan in the center of the oven. Let the pancakes dry for 1 hour or to desired crispness. Watch flatbread carefully. You want them to be dry and crisp but not too browned. Should resemble a wheat cracker in color.

Makes about 3 - 4 small or 2 - 3 larger crackers

* **Not for persons allergic to gluten. Substitute *arrowroot*.**

Flax Seed Crackers

This dehydrator recipe makes a wonderfully crunchy yet filling snack due to the whole flax seeds used.

Virginia

4 C whole *flax seeds*
⅓ - ½ C *Bragg's Liquid Aminos* (depending on desired saltiness)
fresh juice of 2 - 3 lemons

Soak the flax seeds for 4 to 6 hours in 3 cups of water. This releases a sticky substance from the seeds and allows them to hold together. They will also begin to germinate, which increases their nutritional value.

Mix together the soaked flaxseeds, Liquid Aminos, and lemon juice.

Spread the mixture as thinly as possible (approximately ¼ inch thick) on Teflex sheets or fruit leather trays in a dehydrator. Keep your hands wet while you spread the mixture.

Dehydrate at 105 degrees for 5 to 6 hours. Flip the crackers over and remove the Teflex sheets. Continue dehydrating for an additional 4 to 5 hours or until the mixture is completely dry. When completely dry, remove from trays and break into large pieces. Store in an airtight container.

Optional drying method: Pour in a thin layer onto greased cookie sheets. Slowly dry them in a very low oven, about 150 degrees. Watch them carefully in the conventional oven since the drying time will be much shorter due to the higher temperature.

Variations: You may be creative and make up your own recipe. Try adding garlic, onions, carrot juice, Italian seasoning, chili powder, or cumin in many combinations.

Popover Gems

A light and crunchy popover, perfect to serve along side a roast for a special dinner.

1 tsp *butter*
2 *eggs*
1 C almond milk (*see Processes*)
>   **or** ½ C *heavy cream* and ½ C almond milk
>   **or** 1 C *heavy cream*
1 C *tapioca flour*
½ tsp salt

Preheat oven to 425 degrees. Lightly butter large muffin tins or popover pans.

Beat eggs then add milk. Add flour and salt. Whisk together until smooth. It will be a thin batter.

Place buttered muffin tins in the oven about 30 *seconds* to heat. Remove tins from oven; pour batter into heated tins to only ¼ inch deep. Bake for 16 to 18 minutes or until puffed and golden. Remove from tins. Serve immediately. Try variations, below.

Store leftovers in a plastic airtight bag. Refresh their crispness in a 325 degree oven for 2 to 3 minutes or for 2 to 3 seconds in the microwave.

Makes up to 24 popovers

Variations:

>   For a light lunch: Combine flaked tuna, *Homemade Mayonnaise, Bev's Bread and Butter Pickles*, chopped onions, celery, or jicama, and the herbs of your choice. Top the popover and serve with additional *Bread and Butter* pickles.

>   For a quick dessert: Top with *Bev's Custard* or *Chocolate Pudding* and stevia-sweetened whipped heavy cream.

Chapter Seven

Desserts and Snacks

There are a surprising number of desserts, treats, and snacks available on the *LifeChange* diet ~ from Granny Smith apples, berries, and nuts to cream, yogurt, eggs, honey or stevia, and a variety of spices and flavorings. Of course we are not limited to these items, but it is amazing how many recipes have come from this simple list of ingredients.

Conventional diet wisdom says to avoid fats and take care not to add too much sugar to replace it. Sugars, however, are carbohydrates. Carbohydrates are a prime fattening agent and are essential to the life of all fungi.[1]

Fungi cause a wide range of illnesses which often must be battled for a very long time. These desserts and snacks are the menu brighteners that can fit into the *LifeChange* Diet..

The use of conventional sugar substitutes, however, is *not* recommended because they are chemically harmful.[2] Stevia is a natural, safe sweetener that does not affect blood sugar and, therefore, does not feed fungi. Honey can be included sparingly in these diets because it is antifungal.

Special mention should be made regarding nuts. Nuts, particularly walnuts, contain ellagic acid, an anticancer food constituent that is antibacterial and antiviral. The allowed nuts provide a

---

1. Moore-Landecker, E. Fundamentals of the fungi. 4th ed. 1996. Prentice-Hall. Saddle River, NJ.

2. Mercola, Joseph. Aspartame: what you don't know can hurt you. and Splenda is not a 'healthy' sweetener. www.mercola.com

nourishing, satisfying snack on their own and can be chopped, ground, roasted, or used whole in a wide assortment of menu-enhancing creations.

Also, experiment by adding different spices to alter your recipes. Cinnamon, allspice, nutmeg, ginger, mint, lemon or orange peel, or flavoring extracts each contribute strong nutritional properties and their own unique flavors to add further variety to these menu brighters.

Please note: it is very important, whenever possible, to wash the fruit and nuts (*see Processes*) and to always choose organic cream, butter, and eggs and raw honey.

Blueberry Yogurt Soup

This is good hot or cold. The combination I like is organic, whole-milk yogurt with cooked, unsweetened cherries, honey, stevia, and butter. Yum!   *Beverly*

½ tsp powdered or liquid *stevia*
1 tsp grated lemon *zest*
⅛ tsp allspice
2 C water
2 12 oz bags frozen blueberries
1¼ cup plain *yogurt*, divided
2 tbsp fresh lemon juice

In a small skillet, combine stevia, lemon zest, allspice, and water. Place over medium heat. Bring to a boil and cook for 2 minutes to dissolve powdered stevia. Remove from heat.

In a food processor or blender, place the frozen blueberries, 1 cup yogurt, and lemon juice. Add the stevia syrup and purée until smooth.

Serve warm or refrigerate until serving time. Top each serving with 1 tablespoon of the remaining yogurt.

Serves 4

Variations:
    ~ *apple cider vinegar* may be substituted for the lemon juice
    ~ fruit: diced Granny Smith apples, cherries, raspberries, or strawberries, or any desired mix of these can be added
    ~ toppings: use chopped nuts or dried unsweetened cherries
    ~ sweeteners: Add a dollop of *honey* or ⅓ dropper of liquid *stevia*
    ~ flavorings: vanilla and/or almond may be added; also, experiment by adding cinnamon, ginger, or another spice instead of the allspice

Cold Fruit Soup

1 C *yogurt*
1 C fresh or thawed berries
1 tbsp *apple cider vinegar*
1 tbsp lemon juice

Blend all ingredients. Refrigerate any leftovers.

Serves 4

Variations: add slices of Granny Smith apples, nuts, and any
allowed fruit.

Fruit Rave

This is what is commonly known as hot fruit soup. I have
made this recipe for several potluck dinners at work and it is
always a "hit." I rarely have any left to bring home!

Virginia

6 - 10 Granny Smith apples, cored and sliced into chunks
juice of 1 lemon
¼ - ½ C *honey*
1 tsp *stevia*
1 tsp cinnamon, or more to taste
4 20 oz bags frozen berries, unsweetened, any combination
1 - 2 20 oz bags frozen cherries, unsweetened
chopped allowed nuts
heavy cream

Place apples in the bottom of a heavy, large pan or a crock pot. Stir
in the lemon juice, honey, stevia, and cinnamon. Cook till apples are
tender. Add the berries and cherries. Heat through.

To serve, spoon into a cup or bowl. Top with toasted, chopped nuts
and cream to taste, whipped or liquid. For a *pièce de résistance,* add
stevia to the cream prior to whipping it.

Makes 5 quarts

Granny Smith Apples

The versatile Granny Smith apple has a healthful place as a diet brightener. They are useful as treats, snacks, and lunch bag items.

Quick Snack: Apple slices or apple slinkies (made with an apple peeler-corer-slicer) and nuts (*see Nuts* for variations).

Baked: Peel the top half of the apple, core, insert a little honey or stevia, cinnamon, and butter. Wrap in foil for the oven and bake at 350 degrees for about 20 minutes; or place apple in a small glass bowl, cover with a paper towel, and bake in the microwave oven for about 5 minutes.

Apple Chips: Chips are a treat with more than one use. They are good alone or as part of trail mix, etc. Turn to *Apple Chips* for instructions.

See *Tools* for helpful utensils to make these preparations faster and easier.

Fruit Leather

This homemade version of a child's lunchbox staple offers an easy way to prolong the life of fresh fruit. The oven-drying process, which takes about two hours, concentrates the flavors of the fruit beautifully. Dehydration is another, quite easy method used traditionally in Middle Eastern countries;[3] however, it does require a dehydrator (*see Tools* and *Sources*).

Beverly

Oven Method

1 lb ripe allowed fruit: Granny Smith apples, strawberries,
    blueberries, etc., washed and coarsely chopped
1 tsp *stevia* **or** ½ C *honey*

Preheat oven to 200 degrees. Line a baking sheet with parchment paper or oil or grease it with a little butter.

In a medium saucepan, combine fruit and sweetener over low heat. Stir until sweetener is dissolved.

Using an immersion blender or food processor fitted with a steel blade, purée until very smooth. Strain through a fine mesh sieve.

Spread strained fruit mixture evenly over baking sheet. Bake until dry but still tacky, about 2 hours. Cool completely.

Cover surface of fruit with parchment paper. Invert onto a cutting board, parchment side down. Peel off the paper. With a pizza wheel, cut leather in half lengthwise and again in half crosswise, forming four equal rectangles. Cut through parchment with a knife to separate. Roll each rectangle up tightly in parchment paper, beginning

~ *continued, p. 203*

- - - - - - - - - - -
3.   Bell, Mary. Mary Bell's complete dehydration cookbook. 1994. William Morrow and Company, Inc. New York.

with the short side of the fruit that does not have extra parchment paper. This will allow you to peel the fruit from the parchment paper. Store them in an airtight container for up to 2 weeks.

Dehydration Method

The dehydrator's manual will have representative recipes. Some are very simple, such as blending a cored, unpeeled Granny Smith apple and one tomato of about equal size and spreading this on a leather sheet. Dehydrate for eight or more hours. Another leather snack is blending an apple and carrots.

Leathers keep well. Dust the dehydrated leathers with arrowroot, roll up, wrap with plastic wrap, and store in an airtight container. At room temperature they will keep up to a year. If they are refrigerated or frozen, they keep indefinitely.

See *Sources* for information on dehydration book.

Tomato-Apple Leather

Here's a dehydrator treat and wonderful snack for any time. It is interesting and delicious. *Beverly*

Use a large Granny Smith apple and a beefsteak tomato. Remove the stem end of the tomato and the core of the apple. Cut them up and put in a Vitamix™ (*see Tools*) or any high-speed food processor or blender. Run on high until very smooth.

Pour carefully onto a dehydrator's fruit-roll sheet. Dehydrate at about 135 degrees until dry, from 8 to 20 hours depending on your dehydrating unit.

Sprinkle with a little arrowroot and roll up in plastic wrap. Put in airtight storage.

Makes enough to fill 1 dehydrator tray

Note: If the leather is difficult to remove from the dehydrator sheet, place the tray into the freezer until the leather is frozen sufficiently to lift from the tray. Place frozen leather on wax paper to return to room temperature then roll as directed above.

Apple Chips

This recipe has a number of variables: the juiciness of the apples, the humidity of the air, and the process of preparation (frying, dehydrating, or baking). Our recipe was completed by baking.

One problem ~ it's difficult to make them faster than they get eaten! Carrots and tomatoes can also be prepared as chips. I look forward to hearing about variations prepared by our readers. *Beverly*

2 Granny Smith apples
three mixtures, each in a separate bowl:
    ½ lemon, juiced and mixed with 1 C water
    ¼ C melted *butter*
    ¼ C *honey* mixed with 1 C water

Preheat oven to 225 degrees. Line a large baking sheet with baking parchment. Set a wire rack on paper toweling.

Slice the apples very thinly, crosswise through the core (a *mandolin* works nicely). Drop the slices into the lemon-water. Lift out with a strainer; drain briefly.

Drop the slices next into the melted butter. Lift out with the strainer, draining briefly.

Finally, drop the slices into the honey-water mixture. Lift out with the strainer, draining briefly before putting them on the wire rack to drain thoroughly.

Place the slices on the parchment-lined baking sheet. Bake for about an hour. Turn the slices over and continue baking until crisp, may be longer than an hour depending on the individual oven.

Makes enough to fill 1 12" x 15" pan

Cream 'n Berries

A quick ice cream substitute.

½ C *heavy cream*
⅛ tsp *stevia*
½ C frozen berries, any kind or mixture of several

Mix and eat. Add vanilla, cinnamon, or other spice to taste.

Makes 1 serving

Walnut-Coconut Surprise

1 tsp water
½ tsp dehydrated orange *zest*
1 3 oz pkg *cream cheese*
1 tsp lemon *zest*
1 tsp chopped walnuts
¼ C toasted unsweetened coconut (*see Processes*)

Combine water and orange peel in a small bowl. Let stand 15 minutes.

Beat cream cheese until light and fluffy. Add orange peel and the remaining ingredients; combine well.

Roll into balls about a half-teaspoon size. Roll balls in coconut. Serve immediately or store in the refrigerator.

Makes 2 dozen

Note: Though oranges, themselves, are only given as a *Cancer Recommendation*, orange peel is an excellent *nutraceutical* for general diet use. Dehydrate your own orange *zest* to save time and money.

Poached Cherries

This is intense. A little is very satisfying.

1 lb frozen, unsweetened cherries, thawed
1 C water mixed with 2 tbsp cherry concentrate
½ C *honey*
1 vanilla bean with seeds separated from the pod
2 fresh basil leaves
1 3-inch strip of lemon *zest*
¾ C *feta cheese*

Place cherries in a heat-resistant glass bowl and set aside.

In a medium saucepan, combine cherry water, honey, vanilla bean with seeds, basil, and lemon zest. Bring liquid mixture to a boil over medium-high heat. Pour hot liquid over cherries and set aside to cool to room temperature. Cherries should be slightly soft. It takes about an hour.

Drain the cherries but reserve the poaching liquid in the saucepan. Discard the basil, vanilla bean, seeds, and lemon zest. Boil this liquid until it has reduced to about half. Pour hot liquid over cherries. Chill at least one hour or overnight.

Serve with a spoonful of feta cheese.

Serves 4

Cherry or Blueberry Gelatin

A healthy, delicious gelatin to be used in all the ways we have used sugar-laden, artificially-colored gelatin. The color and taste come from real fruit. These fruits have natural health-giving antioxidants and *phytochemicals* that have been researched in many scientific studies and reported as advantageous for general health and treatment of cancer.

Beverly

2 C water, divided
1 envelope gelatin
2 - 3 tbsp *honey*
⅛ tsp (½ dropper) liquid *stevia*
2 - 3 tbsp cherry or blueberry concentrate (*see Sources*)

Place ¼ cup of water in a small saucepan. Empty gelatin into the water and let sit for 5 minutes to soften. Add remaining water and warm over low heat, stirring constantly, until the gelatin mixture is clear. Remove from heat to cool.

Add the honey and stevia, stir until dissolved. Stir in the cherry or blueberry concentrate. Pour into the serving container and refrigerate until gelled. Add fruit or vegetables, if desired, to the gelatin when it is semi-gelled.

Serves 4

Dream Puff Cream

¼ C water
1 envelope gelatin
1 C frozen unsweetened cherries
1 C chopped nuts
2 C *heavy cream*

Set a small mixing bowl into a bigger bowl containing ice and water or set the small mixing bowl in the freezer.

Place ¼ cup of water in a small saucepan. Empty gelatin into the water and let sit for 5 minutes to soften. Warm over low heat, stirring constantly, until the gelatin mixture is clear. Remove from heat to cool.

Chop the frozen cherries and the nuts; set aside.

Pour the cream into the small, cold mixing bowl. Begin to slowly beat the cream. Pour the gelatin mixture into the cream while whipping slowly until gelatin is fully incorporated. Increase the beater speed and whip until the cream mixture forms soft peaks.

Fold in the chopped cherries and nuts. Gently pour into a serving bowl and refrigerate until set.

Serves 4

Baked Apple Dessert

1 Granny Smith apple per serving, peeled if desired
2 tbsp melted *butter*
$\frac{1}{4}$ - $\frac{1}{2}$ tsp *stevia*
3 tbsp hot tap water
1 - 2 tsp cinnamon, to taste

Preheat oven to 350 degrees. Grease an ovenproof baking dish.

Slice or dice the apples, as you prefer. Dip into melted butter and drain. Place in lightly buttered pan.

Stir stevia into hot water; sprinkle over the apples. Sprinkle apples with cinnamon. Bake about 30 minutes or until tender.

Serve with whipped cream sweetened with stevia.

Makes 1 serving each

Nuts

Nuts are versatile ~ they can be used in many types of recipes, and their ellagic acid food constituent and essential oils make them very healthful, as well.

Before using nuts in recipes

Wash and dry all raw nuts before eating "as is" or making any other nut treats (*see Processes*). Washing nuts helps prepare them to be a healthier food by eliminating dirt and any fungi present. In addition, they taste better.

Buttered Nut Snack

Preheat oven to 275 degrees. Melt butter in a cookie sheet with short sides. Stir in nuts to coat with the butter. Bake until lightly roasted; stir and check every 20 minutes. If the oven temperature is increased, the nuts will roast faster, but you must watch carefully not to over-brown or burn them. Salt, if desired.

Sticky Treat

Mix together ¼ cup water and 3 tablespoons honey in a sprayed, non-stick skillet. Add nuts until about 1 inch deep. Cook, stirring over low to medium heat until the moisture has evaporated. Place in a greased serving dish.

Spiced Nut Variation: Add small amounts of spices such as cloves, nutmeg, cinnamon, or ginger to the honey mixture.

Pie Crust.

An adaptation of the *Sticky Treat* makes a good pie crust. Chop small or finely grind the *un*cooked nuts, then proceed as described in *Sticky Treat*. Press into pie plate; you may need to add 1 to 2 tablespoons melted butter to attain the needed consistency.

Dessert Topping

Use any one of these suggestions as a creative topping for *Fruit Rave, Custard,* yogurt, sliced fresh fruits, or other dessert and snacks.

Crusts

LifeChange Crust

¼ C *tapioca flour*
¼ C *heavy cream*
pinch salt
touch of *honey* or *stevia*, as desired
spice, as desired

Combine all ingredients. Press into a pie pan.

For unfilled shell: Bake for 10 to 12 minutes or until lightly browned.
Will have a slightly bumpy surface.

For filled shell: bake as usual.

Makes 1 crust

Nut Crust

4 tbsp melted *butter*
4 tsp cinnamon
2 C nut meal

Combine. Press into a pie pan.

Makes 1 crust

Oat Crust ~ A *Step-Up Level* recipe.

1 C rolled oats
¾ C brazil nuts, chopped
2 tsp cumin
4 tbsp *butter,* melted
4 tsp salt

Mix well and press into pie pan.

Makes 1 crust

Strawberry Bavarian Pie

2 pints fresh strawberries, divided
1 C *yogurt* cheese (*see Processes*)
1 envelope unflavored gelatin
½ C water
½ tsp *stevia*
2 tsp lemon juice
9 inch *Nut Crust* (*see Crusts*)

Thinly slice 1½ pints of strawberries; reserve remaining ½ pint for garnish. Place sliced strawberries in a large bowl and gently fold in yogurt cheese.

In a sauce pan, soften gelatin in water then place over low heat and stir until gelatin dissolves. Add stevia, lemon juice, and dissolved gelatin to the sliced strawberries. Chill until mixture mounds when dropped from a spoon.

Pour into nut crust. Decorate with whole strawberries and chill.

Serves 8

Variation: place a tablespoon of nut crust mixture into bottom of muffin tins. Fill with chilled strawberry mixture. Makes 12 to 14 individual tarts.

Fantasy Yogurt Cheesecake

2 C *yogurt* cheese (see *Processes*)
½ tsp *stevia* **or** 2 - 4 tbsp *honey*
1 tsp vanilla
1 tbsp *arrowroot*
2 *eggs*, lightly beaten

Preheat oven to 325 degrees.

Combine yogurt cheese, sweetener, vanilla, and arrowroot powder. Add eggs and mix gently with a fork or wire whisk. Pour into an 8 inch pie pan or 7 inch springform pan.

Bake 20 to 25 minutes for the pie pan or 55 minutes for the springform pan. Cool slightly and refrigerate, uncovered, for 24 hours.

Serves 8

Note: The cheesecake will be firmer if you drain the yogurt up to 24 hours. Yogurt cheese may be kept in a covered container in the refrigerator until you have enough for the recipe.

Bev's Custard

A very smooth, delicious custard you can serve in several ways. Spoon it into a nut crust, sprinkle the top with prepared nuts or allowed fruit. It could also be frozen to make "ice cream."

2 C *heavy cream*
⅛ - ¼ tsp *stevia*, liquid or powder
1 tbsp *honey*
2 *eggs*
1 tsp vanilla
dash of salt
cinnamon or nutmeg to sprinkle on top, if desired

Preheat oven to 325 degrees. Butter an ovenproof glass baking dish.

Scald cream, stevia, and honey in double boiler.

Beat eggs with vanilla and salt in a separate bowl. Slowly stir hot cream mixture into egg mixture. Pour into buttered baking dish.

Place baking dish inside an ovenproof pan; add one inch of warm water to the large pan. Bake 30 minutes until set or when inserted knife comes out clean.

Remove custard from the hot water when you take it out of the oven or it will overcook. Dust with cinnamon or nutmeg and serve.

Serves 4

Individual Carmel Custards

⅓ C *honey*
2 tbsp water
1 recipe of *Bev's Custard*

Preheat oven to 325 degrees. *Butter* or spray muffin tins or small ovenproof bowls with *nonstick spray.*

Mix honey and water in a small sauce pan. Cook honey mixture over medium-low heat until slightly reduced.

Pour a layer of the honey mixture into each individual container and add custard to fill each cup to slightly under the rim.

Set muffin tins into a larger, flat ovenproof baking dish and add 1 inch of water; be careful not to get any water in the custard. Bake until the custards are set, approximately 30 minutes.

Invert onto individual serving dishes and serve warm with a sprinkling of chopped nuts, a sprinkling of cinnamon, or a sprig of fresh mint.

Serves 4

Dairy-Free Custard

Be ready for this very nice lactose-free custard to separate slightly as it cools.

2 C almond milk, unsweetened (*see Processes*)
3 *eggs*
1 tbsp *honey*
⅛ tsp *stevia*

Preheat oven to 325 degrees. Grease individual custard cups or one large custard dish with *butter* or *nonstick spray*.

In a medium-large double boiler, combine all ingredients and heat to scalding, about 150 degrees on a candy thermometer. Pour into greased containers.

Place dishes in a baking dish and add 1 inch of hot water to large dish; be careful not to splash water into the custards. Bake for 25 to 35 minutes for small dishes, 50 to 60 minutes for a large dish.

Serves 4

Chocolate Pudding

This rich pudding is a *Step*Up Level* recipe because chocolate is made from cocoa beans. I find the smaller serving quite satisfying.

This is a good recipe for experimentation. Try it with unsweetened baking chocolate. Add whipped cream on top to serve.   *Beverly*

2 *eggs*
½ C *honey*
¼ tsp clear liquid *stevia*
¼ C unsweetened baking cocoa
3 tbsp *arrowroot*
¼ tsp salt
2¼ C almond milk (*see Processes*)
2 tbsp *butter*
1 tsp vanilla
allowed nuts, finely chopped, for garnish

In a large microwavable glass bowl, whisk eggs thoroughly.

In a tall, narrow pan (to confine the powder), combine honey, stevia, cocoa, arrowroot, and salt. Add to the eggs and whisk to combine. Gradually stir in the almond milk. Whisk ingredients thoroughly.

Cover the bowl and place in the microwave. Microwave for 2 minutes and 20 seconds. Whisk thoroughly.

Repeat the heating and whisking steps two more times, then stir in the butter and vanilla.

Spoon into six pudding cups or small serving bowls. Cover with finely chopped allowed nuts.

Serves 6

Thornhill Fudge *- Adapted for the LifeChange Diet*

I adapted this rich treat from my father's recipe. The original recipe is unacceptable on an antifungal diet, but this recipe is acceptable on the *Step·Up Level* because cocoa is made from beans.

The recipe will not "nougat" like fudge made with sugar. It *will* thicken and become like a hard caramel when refrigerated. Place in small cupcake or candy papers to make it easier to serve. Do not eat a lot of this, but use it as a special treat.

Beverly

3 tbsp unsweetened baking cocoa
½ C *heavy cream*
¾ C *honey*
⅓ tsp *stevia*
2 tbsp *butter*
½ tsp vanilla
1 C chopped pecans, walnuts, or other allowed nuts

Combine cocoa, cream, and honey in a large pan. Cook on the stove to 236 degrees on a candy thermometer, stirring frequently. Add the stevia near the end of cooking. Remove from heat and add butter and vanilla. Stir until butter is dissolved and mixed into the cocoa mixture.

Place in a pan of cold water to cool; be careful ***not*** to get any water in the mixture. Stir while it is cooling. As it begins to thicken, add the chopped nuts.

Pour onto a greased plate or drop by spoonfuls into miniature cupcake or candy papers.

Makes about 1 pound

Snow Ice Cream

How could we resist? Half of us are from Minnesota!

1 C *heavy cream*, cold
½ tsp vanilla
1 scant tbsp *stevia*
4 - 5 C clean, unpacked snow

In a large, chilled ceramic or stainless steel bowl, mix cream, vanilla, and stevia. Slowly add the snow, stirring constantly until as thick as ice cream.

Makes more than 4 dozen spoonfuls

Variation: Try adding cinnamon or other flavoring extracts to cream mixture.

Chapter Eight

Beverages

Many people are drawn to certain beverages at predictable times and circumstances: coffee during break at work, diet soda with lunch, a glass of wine for dinner. To break unhealthy beverage habits takes effort. Changes must be made. Coffee, tea, soft drinks, alcohol ~ all are hindrances to conquering fungal infection.

Conversations abound on the diet scene regarding whether or not coffee and tea are healthy beverages. Changing the coffee and tea habit is important to those who have become dependent upon these drinks. A test for dependency is whether you experience headaches or other observable symptoms of withdrawal when you stop drinking them. Monitor yourself - and gear up for an all-out fight for good health.

Pop, soda, soda pop, whatever the local name, soft drinks are the choice of a staggering number of Americans for their liquid refreshment ... and offer the consumer unwitting consumption of copious amounts of sugar. Diet soft drinks can be a worse choice than the sugar-laden ones. Diet drinks often contain aspartame (NutraSweet™), sucralose (Splenda™), or some other artificial sweetener. These substances are harmful (*see LifeChange Diet ~ Sweeteners*). An added benefit to change: you may find you save a significant amount of money if you replace the soft drinks in your diet with healthy alternatives.

Alcoholic drinks in any form are counter productive. Fungi are an integral part of the production of alcohol since fungi are always involved in any fermentation process.[1] Consider the following two excerpts from the fields of agricultural science and mycology:

---

1. Kaufmann, D. A. The germ that causes cancer. 2002. 22,86-87,153-154. MediaTrition. Rockwall, TX.

Food is not poisonous. However, toxigenic fungi and their mycotoxins are always present in stored foods (grains for manufacturing the beer) and in fermented beverages (fungi are essential to the fermenting process). Fungi and mycotoxins are heat tolerant. Heat processes (boiling, baking, etc.) are absent from any recommendations for managing fungi and mycotoxins in bringing food products to the consumer because heat is ineffective in controlling fungi.[2]

Fungi must be dealt with in the harvest, storage, and initial food handling processes or the fungi and their mycotoxins are extremely difficult to eliminate. Thus, from contaminated grains through to fermentation, the process used to make beer constitutes a significant way to place humans at risk.[3]

Conquering a fungal infection can have an added benefit: a lessened dependence on alcoholic beverages.

This chapter gives you a number of flavorful hot and cold beverage choices to fit this niche in the food day. To give thought to healthy beverage choices is a step on the way to improved health. "Eating out" choices are as easy as requesting your preference of hot or cold water with a slice of lemon or lime.

2. Council for Agricultural Science and Technology (CAST). Mycotoxins: economic and health risks. Task force report 116. CAST. Nov. 1989. *in* Hunt, B. T. Fungazette Vol 2. No. 4. 7. 2000. MediaTrition. Rockwall, TX.

3. Costantini, A. V. Wieland, H. Qvick, M. D. Fungalbionics: the fungal/mycotoxin etiology of human disease. Vol. II: Cancer. 1994. Johann Friedrich Verlag. Freiburg, Germany. *in* Hunt, B. T. Fungazette Vol 2. No. 4. 7. 2000. MediaTrition. Rockwall, TX

Flavored Waters

Ginger Mint Water

1 4inch piece ginger, scrubbed and peeled and finely minced
3 sprigs fresh mint
2 qts spring water

Use a mortar and pestle to crush the ginger. Crush the mint. Combine water, ginger, and mint in large pitcher. Let steep for 1 hour before serving over ice.

Serves 8

Cucumber Water

1 medium cucumber, scrubbed well
2 qts spring water

Remove strips of cucumber skin, creating wide, alternating bands of peeled and bare cucumber. Trim and discard ends. Halve cucumber lengthwise; cut into quarter-inch slices. Combine cucumber and water in large pitcher; steep for 1 hour and serve over ice.

Serves 8

Lime Rosemary Water

2 qts spring water
2 limes, cut into ¼-inch slices
2 sprigs fresh rosemary, broken into small pieces
¼ tsp *orange oil*

Combine water, limes, rosemary, and orange oil in a large pitcher. Let it steep for 1 hour before serving over ice.

Serves 8

Smoothies

A great way to start the morning! Experiment with different fruit and vegetable combinations. Try adding ground flax seed or psyllium hulls for a fiber boost.

Basic Apple Smoothie

1 Granny Smith apple, cored but unpeeled, cut into chunks
4 tbsp *heavy cream*
stevia, to taste
1 tsp lemon juice
pinch of apple pie spice
ice cubes

In a blender container, combine all ingredients except the ice. Begin to process; add ice cubes as it blends until you achieve desired consistency.

Serves 1

Basic Morning Smoothie

⅓ C baby carrots
1 Granny Smith apple, cored but unpeeled, cut into chunks
⅓ C berries, fresh or frozen ~ your choice: strawberries, blueberries, raspberries, cranberries, or other
⅛ tsp *stevia* extract
1 tbsp ground *flax seed* (optional)
ice cubes

In a blender container, combine all ingredients except the ice. Begin to process; add ice cubes as it blends until you achieve desired consistency.

Serves 1 - 2

LifeChange Veggie Smoothie

¾ - 1 C fresh vegetables, cut into chunks (see list, below)
1 tomato, peeled and seeded
2 tbsp organic *apple cider vinegar*
2 tbsp *heavy cream*
salt and pepper, to taste
1 tsp herbs or spices, to taste (see list, below)
ice cubes

In a blender container, combine all ingredients except the ice. Begin to process; add ice cubes as it blends until you achieve desired consistency.

Serves 1

Basic vegetable options: red or green bell pepper, cucumber, radishes, onion, carrots, celery, spinach, beets

Also try: cubed, parboiled celeriac, yucca, or squash; or beet greens, celery leaves, or more exotic lettuces

Basic herb and spice options: tarragon, garlic, cumin, dill, rosemary, ginger, lemon zest, basil, oregano, clove

Zippy Hot Lemon Drink

Squeeze the juice of one-half lemon into a cup or mug.

Add 1 tbsp *honey*
    1 tbsp cherry or blueberry concentrate
    $\frac{1}{8}$ tsp liquid *stevia*.

Fill the cup with boiling water. Enjoy!

Serves 1

Chapter Nine

LifeChange Support

- Processes, Sources, Tips, and Tools -

Changes in eating habits can be both difficult and discouraging. To eliminate breads, sugar, and potatoes then include unusual vegetable items, plus meet organic standards, will add both time and money to every food consideration or meal plan.

This chapter is to help you learn the important processes, incorporate helpful tips, discover useful tools, and access potential sources to not only help with *LifeChange* meal planning and preparation but to also help you manage time and money. The processes will assist in the "learning curve" involved in the incorporation of new habits. And, as we continue to say: you are part of this, we welcome your feed back and suggestions.

- *Processes* -

Baking Powder

Double-acting baking powder needs to be fresh ~ it has a "use by" date. You can store the separate ingredients for make-your-own single-acting baking powder in case you run out of it or exceed the use-by date. The individual ingredients do not age as long as they are stored separately, so make only the amount needed for each recipe.

A single-acting baking powder must be cooked soon after the liquid is added to the recipe or it will go flat. The leavening action takes place when the liquid ingredients are added to the recipe.

Plan for one tablespoon of the following mixture for each cup of flour in the recipe. Mix ingredients and incorporate into the dry ingredients of the recipe. Mix in the liquid ingredients immediately prior to placing recipe into the oven. The recipe must be placed in the oven quickly, before it goes flat.

For 1 teaspoon of single-acting baking powder mix:
$\frac{1}{4}$ tsp baking soda
$\frac{1}{2}$ tsp cream of tartar
$\frac{1}{4}$ tsp *arrowroot*

For 1 tablespoon of single-acting baking powder mix:
$\frac{3}{4}$ tsp baking soda
$1\frac{1}{2}$ tsp cream of tartar
$\frac{3}{4}$ tsp *arrowroot*

Mix these dry ingredients together and add to the dry ingredients of your recipe. Add liquid immediately before cooking.

℘ ⋈

Dairy

Homemade Sour Cream

2 C *heavy cream*
1 tbsp *vinegar* or lemon juice

Stir together and let stand for a few minutes. Refrigerate.

Makes 2 cups

Clarified Butter/Ghee

Ghee does not burn as quickly as butter. It can also be stored longer.

1 lb unsalted *butter*, cut into pieces

In a small saucepan, heat the butter over low heat until completely melted. Simmer gently for 10 minutes. Remove from the heat and let stand for 10 minutes.

Skim off the milk solids that rise to the top. Carefully pour off the clear yellow butter into a glass jar with a tight fitting lid. Discard the milk solids which settled out of the liquid.

Refrigerate up to 3 weeks or freeze until needed.

Makes about 1½ cups

Stablized Whipping Cream

This can be used as a topping for desserts, hot drinks, or any thing where a cream "dollop" or spread is used.

For each cup of *heavy cream* use
    1 tsp gelatin
    2 tbsp water
    2 tbsp *honey*

In a small sauce pan, mix gelatin with water to soften. Heat on low until melted. Add the honey to the gelatin mixture and cool to room temperature.

Whip cream until it begins to mound. Continue beating and slowly add the gelatine mixture. Beat until the cream stiffens. Store in an airtight container in the refrigerator.

Yogurt Cheese

The Process

Yogurt cheese is made by draining the liquid from unflavored *yogurt* ~ yogurt that does NOT contain gelatin. This is a home process, very easy to do. On the market, you can find "yogurt funnels," but it can also be done easily with readily available kitchen equipment.

You will need a medium-large sieve and cheesecloth or a large paper coffee filter. Place the sieve over a large mouth jar, large coffee mug, or a bowl. The vessel should be tall enough that the bottom of the sieve will not come in contact with the whey that will drain out (about 4 ounces of whey from an 8 ounce yogurt or 8 ounces of whey from a 16 ounce yogurt). Line the sieve with the cheesecloth or paper coffee filter.

~ continued, pg. 232

Spoon out enough yogurt to fill your sieve, then place the yogurt-filled sieve with the container into the refrigerator. Allow the whey to drain out until you have the desired consistency: 8 to 12 hours for most uses, 14 or more for cream cheese consistency.

To unmold, invert the yogurt cheese onto a plate; peel the paper or cheesecloth from the yogurt cheese and discard. The liquid whey contains the same beneficial cultures present in the yogurt and you may utilize it in any recipe you desire. It is suitable to drink, if you have a liking for it. Otherwise you may discard the whey. Store the yogurt cheese in a covered container in the refrigerator.

How to use Yogurt Cheese

Yogurt cheese can be used instead of cream cheese, sour cream, or mayonnaise in many of your favorite recipes. Yogurt cheese mixes easily with a fork. Vigorous beating with a blender or food processor is not recommended.

When using yogurt cheese in place of mayonnaise, retain the mayonnaise flavor by combining 2 parts yogurt cheese with 1 part *Homemade Mayonnaise*.

Like all milk products, yogurt cheese is sensitive to heat ~ do not heat it alone or allow it to boil. To cook with yogurt cheese, combine with *arrowroot* or *eggs* to prevent separation or thinning.

When possible, add yogurt cheese to hot foods at the end of cooking time:

~ bring the yogurt cheese to room temperature and allow the hot food to cool slightly, **or**
~ stir a small amount of hot food into the yogurt cheese to warm it before slowly adding the warmed yogurt cheese into the hot food, stirring constantly.

                                                    ଔ   ଔ

Food Dehydration[1]

Dehydration is a way to take advantage of sales and in-season produce and to preserve those foods for later use. It is simpler than canning, not only in preparation but also in the clean up and food storage. Dehydration also retains more inherent food value because the process requires less heat and no water. Dried food has a long shelf life ~ one year at room temperature and indefinitely when refrigerated or frozen. In addition to preserving fruit, vegetables, and meat, you can make leathers and use those leathers to make sauces.

Advantages of Dehydrating Foods

~ one-time equipment cost

~ can choose quality foods for later use

~ supply can be built for easy access to safe, good foods

~ money saving: can take advantage of specials and in-season foods

~ you can choose pesticide and chemical-free foods

~ creative recycling: cuts down on packaging

~ space saving

~ finished product is light weight

~ process is not complicated

~ healthy: vitamins and minerals are not altered or depleted

~ continued, p. 234

---

1. Bell, Mary. Mary Bell's complete dehydrator cookbook. 1994. William Morrow and Co., Inc. NY.

Safety in Dehydrating Foods

~ sanitary procedures are essential since organisms that cause
     spoilage are always present in the environment

~ be sure the product is thoroughly dry or it will mold

~ meat needs a steady internal temperature of 145 degrees for 45
     minutes to effectively kill microbes, illustrating the importance
     of accurate temperature management

~ store dried foods in the freezer to insure viability

My motto is to use the foods I've dried within a year, in
other words, from season to season. Use your dried tomatoes
before they come in season again. It is a good policy, it
gets you in the habit of turning to your dry supply instead of
running to the store. Dried foods do loose color and flavor
when stored too long.[2]

෨ ෬

2. Bell, Mary. www.drystore.com/drypages/drywoman.html. March 2004.

Herbs

Spices and herbs can serve to add flavor interest to food preparation. We recommend that you research your own cookbook or go to the library to personalize your own venture into new tastes.

Herbs are best fresh but, in reality, we need to preserve them to prevent waste and to have the flavor we desire when a fresh picked herb is not available. Drying herbs is the way to have a ready supply. You can dry herbs in the refrigerator or in a dehydrator.

To use the refrigerator, wash and dry the herbs, then roll them loosely in tulle. Tie the ends of the fabric. Refrigerate for about two weeks or until they are dry and crumbly. Store in an air-tight container in the refrigerator.

To dehydrate herbs, follow the instructions from the dehydrator's manufacturer (*see Tools*).

Hints about a few herbs

~ basil - essential to Italian flavoring; complements meat, fish, poultry, and many vegetables

~cardamom - interestingly, both Scandinavian and Indian cooking use this warmly-sweet spice; goes well with fruit soups, baked apples, meat balls, squash, and sweet potatoes

~ cilantro - has a love/hate reputation; use fresh because cilantro retains little flavor when dried; sprinkle over grilled chicken or fish or over ripe tomatoes or an unsandwich

~ marjoram - a kin to oregano; use with tomato-based recipes, summer squash, fish, lamb, and veal

~ thyme - a strong yet versatile herb; use with tomato recipes, vegetable soup, beef stew, poultry stuffing, and summer squash

℘ ℂ

Juices

For the cancer patient, fresh-squeezed fruit juice may be appealing to a flagging appetite. Do not use canned, bottled, or frozen juices. Using a juicing machine can be helpful. Also, the Vitamix™ machine is powerful enough to make smoothies from suitable fruit or vegetables. With this appliance the valuable fiber is retained. It makes noticeably smoother drinks (*see Sources*).

☙ ❧

Marinating

A marinade generally refers to a seasoned liquid used to tenderize and flavor meat, fish, or poultry. It consists of oil, acid, and spices. A marinade is meant to be drawn into the meat, altering the environment into one more hostile to organisms. The occurrence of added flavoring is only a secondary benefit.

A proper marinade is high acid and salt. The purpose of the acid is to break down the fibers to tenderize the meat; the salt draws out the water and the organisms suspended in it. Both the acid-breakdown and the salt are antiseptic.

Proper marinating requires the meat to be totally covered by the marinade. If this is not true, the exchange of fluids will be incomplete. Always marinate in the refrigerator. Use only a glazed ceramic, glass, stainless steel, or plastic holding vessel, never aluminum. Use only food-grade plastic bags to marinate in a bag.

General Rules for Marinating[3]

~ use room temperature marinade over raw meat

~ *reserve* any marinade to be used as a sauce *before* the remainder is poured over the meat

~ use a glass container to prevent reaction to the acid

~ marinate seafood for only 30 to 60 minutes, chicken up to two hours, and other meats up to 24 hours completely submerged in liquid marinade

~ drain before cooking; remove submerged meat from the marinade and completely dispose of the used liquid marinade

℘   date

---

3. Better Homes and Gardens. April 1994.

Nuts, Almond Milk, and Nut Snacks

Nut milks can take the place of dairy milks in most recipes. They are an excellent drink, and by making your own you can adjust the richness to your taste. Nut milks are used as a base for soups and smoothies, in gravies and sauces. It is difficult to find an acceptable source for commercial, unsweetened nut milks...so make your own!

Nut and seed milks can be made from almost any raw nut or seed. The best and most nutritious choices are almonds and sesame seeds, but pecans, walnuts, and cashews also deliver great results. For a richer, thicker recipe, add a tablespoon of whole flax seed to any of these milks. Refrigerate all nut milks and use within 2 days. Use *GSE*® in the soak water to increase the storage time. Also, filtered water affects the results in a positive way. Experiment to see how your circumstances extend the storage life.

To make nut milk, the nuts need to be soaked. Nuts are seeds, therefore have all the nutrients required for growth. Soaking is similar to sprouting ~ the nuts and seeds bathe in water though the nuts are not soaked long enough for germination to finish. The goal in soaking is to change the consistency of the nut.

The process of soaking actually begins the germination process; it activates the vitamins, minerals, proteins, and essential fatty acids which are dormant in the raw seed or nut. This high protein content is why body builders often use nuts in their diet. Soaked nuts can be eaten as they are. In fact, soaking makes them easier to chew and digest.

Soaking Nuts

The basic ratio for soaking is 1 cup nuts to 3 to 6 cups of water, depending upon size of seed or nut. Use filtered room temperature water and add 15 drops of *GSE*®. In a glass bowl or container, cover the nuts or seeds with the *GSE*® solution and let soak for the following times:

small nuts/seeds ~ soak for 5 hours
hulled nuts/seeds ~ soak for 6 - 8 hours
large nuts/seeds ~ soak for 12 hours

After soaking, drain and rinse well; add fresh water to the glass storage container, and refrigerate. Change the water every 2 to 3 days[4] since the nuts or seeds are now alive and shed metabolic products into the water.

Almond Milk

1 C soaked, drained almonds
6 C purified water

In the container of a food processor or blender, process half the nuts with half of the water for 3 minutes. Strain into a storage container. If richer milk is desired, reduce the water for the second half to be blended.

Note: If you use a Vitamix™, process for only 2 minutes. Straining is not necessary.

ᔎ ᧚

---

4. Calabro, R. L. Living in the raw: recipes for a healthy lifestyle. 1998. Rose Publishing Company. Santa Cruz, CA.

Recipe Thickener/Roux

Use to thicken liquids. This thickener is bland so it will mix well with meats, vegetables, or fruit dishes.

Making a thickener/roux for gravies and sauces

½ C non-hydrogenated shortening, meat fat (use recommended sources), *coconut oil*, or *ghee/clarified butter*
½ C *arrowroot* powder

Melt the fat in a skillet over a low heat. Add the arrowroot. Cook while stirring on low to medium heat until there is some color.

Store in the refrigerator.

Makes approximately ¾ cup

Gravy

Pour pan drippings into a larger measuring cup, add water to equal the number of cups of gravy desired. Pour into sauce pan and whisk in 2 tablespoons thickener/roux for each cup of liquid. Bring to a low boil, whisking constantly, and continue to boil until gravy reaches desired thickness.

Stews, soups, meat pies, or cobblers

In a small bowl, mix 1 or 2 tablespoons of thickener/roux with some of the liquid from the recipe or a tablespoon of water. Add to the remainder of the recipe's liquid. Stir well. Repeat until the liquid is thickened to suit the recipe.

ഔ   ങ

Stock, Broth, and Soup

Make your own broths, stocks, or soups ~ hearty, tasty, fast, and satisfying! The key is preparing ahead.

Soup

Generally, soup is

stock or broth + vegetables + meat

Build a supply of soup ingredients: dried, refrigerated, or frozen.

Stock or Broth

Make your own stock or broth with leftover bones or bones from the butcher. Boil left over bones from any meat served…even the ones left on family member's plates. Adele Davis wrote long ago about this, reminding the cook that broth made this way is sterilized by the long boiling procedure. Of course, broth can be made from bones purchased for the purpose, too.

Place the bones in a pan deep enough to completely cover the bones with water. Add enough water to cover; simmer for two to three hours. Strain, reserving any meat in the pot for use in the soup. Freeze in pint containers or refrigerate to use within 2 to 3 days.

Vegetables

For prepare-ahead convenience, steam a large quantity of vegetables. Use a variety of fresh, prepared-ahead, or leftover vegetables and steam them by individual kind, then blend the cooked vegetables and refrigerate or freeze in useable, pint quantities. Puréed vegetables will add a creamy consistency to soup.

~ continued, p. 242

Meat

Prepare allowable meat of your choice. Use cooked meat, leftovers, or meat purchased and cooked for this use. Cut into bite-size pieces, heat, and flavor to suit. Store in useable quantities in the refrigerator or freezer.

Assemble Soup

Combine prepared-ahead stock, vegetables, and meat. Heat. Flavor to suit. If you like "creamed" soup, add 1 to 2 table-spoons of *heavy cream* to each individual steaming bowl. Serve with crisp vegetables for some crunch as well as *Crispy Flatbread, Flax Seed Crackers*, or *Popover Gems*.

ം   ര

Tapioca Flour

Tapioca flour is lighter both in texture and in weight than standard wheat flour, so it tends to "cloud" into the air if handled roughly or quickly.

Liquids must be stirred into the tapioca flour to facilitate absorption, but then the flour does absorb moisture very quickly ~ almost like a sponge. Just as with wheat flour, this property allows a wide variety of tapioca flour uses, from thickening broth to making biscuits.

The key to the use of tapioca flour is thorough cooking. When underbaked, tapioca flour will be spongey in texture and very chewy. It rises very well, so make smaller portions and cook it for the full time period indicated in each recipe.

Tapioca is also versatile in its partnering with other food ingredients. The flour has a natural sweetness that works well in dessert recipes, but also with entrées. When poured in a thin layer, it bakes to a golden brown flakiness, so it makes excellent soup crackers and pie crusts. When used in the pancake and biscuit recipes, its fluffy texture holds together well and tastes wonderful as small dumplings in a chicken stew or with berries, honey, or cream for breakfast.

80 CB

Tapioca self-rising flour

For each cup of *tapioca flour*, whisk in
    5 tsp single or double-acting baking powder
    $\frac{1}{8}$ tsp salt

80 CB

Unsweetened Coconut

Toasting

Melt 2 to 3 tablespoons of *butter*. Pour over 1 cup of unsweetened coconut. Toss to coat then drain well. Reserve any leftover melted butter for additional batches.

Place coconut on parchment-lined baking sheet with sides. Bake in a 210 degree oven until lightly browned. Check often and use caution since coconut browns easily. Cool on a rack. Store in an airtight container in the refrigerator or freezer.

Trail Mix

A favorite treat! The recipe can vary somewhat with one's personal preferences. It is basically nuts, unsweetened coconut, dried cherries, and *Apple Chips*.

Carefully butter and brown the nuts of your choice and the coconut ~ remember: they brown easily. Drain the excess butter from them before browning. Make *Apple Chips*.

Combine equal amounts of coconut, nuts, unsweetened dried cherries; add *Apple Chips* just prior to serving the *Trail Mix*. If the mix is stored as a mixture, the apples will tend to lose their crispness.

℅   ଔ

Washing and Drying Produce and Nuts

Today, the recommendation to wash fruit and vegetables comes from many sources. We would expand this to include the washing of all nuts. Washing fruit and vegetables with grapefruit seed extract (*GSE*® ~ *see Sources*) extends the time your produce will stay fresh.

Washing Produce

Prewash produce of any sand or dirt. In a ceramic, glass, or stainless steel bowl, add 15 drops of *GSE*® for every 2 cups of filtered water needed to submerge the produce. Leave the produce submerged for 2 or 3 minutes. Drain in a colander. There is no need to rinse the GSE off the produce.

Disposable spinner for drying produce

Prepare a standard plastic grocery bag with handles: fold a section of newspaper to fit the bottom of the bag; cover newspaper with several clean paper towels. The newspaper retains water and the paper towel protects the produce from the newsprint.

Place washed produce into the prepared bag and sling the bag in a circular motion to dry the produce.

For greens: After drying, separate produce in a single layer on a kitchen towel. Roll jellyroll fashion and refrigerate. You now have greens ready for salads or for cooking. After rinsing with GSE, they will keep fresh for a week.

~ continued, p. 246

Washing Nuts

The process of rinsing and drying nuts allows them to taste fresher and prepares them for use in recipes.

Add 15 drops of *GSE*® to 2 cups of filtered, room temperature water. Empty up to a 1 pound package of allowable nuts into the solution. If using more than 1 pound of nuts, use the same solution to wash 1 pound at a time. Do not rinse. Drain in a colander.

Spread a single layer of washed nuts on a cookie sheet with sides. Dry in a 200 degree oven or a dehydrator at 95 degrees.

Check periodically and remove when dry ~ do not allow the nuts to brown. Drying time varies according to type of nut and how long the nuts were left in the GSE solution. Store in an airtight container in the refrigerator or freezer.

൯   ൙

- Sources -

Sources mentioned in this book who have effective alternative products

<u>*BioActive Nutrients*</u>
vitamins, minerals, antifungal kits

Guy Evans, owner
www.bioactivenutrients.com
1.800.879.6504

<u>*Orange TKO Midwest*</u>
TKO can clean everything around the house as well as help with insect control.

Barb and Frank Long, owners
www.orangetkomidwest.com
1.866.698.7856

<u>*Bio Innovations*</u>
noni juice, vitamins, personal products, and information on healthy living

Dr. Richard Becker, owner
2045 Kristy Lane
Rockwall, TX 75032
www.phaseonenoni.com
1.888.442.5150

<u>*Nutritional Living*</u>
supplements, nutrients, nutritional information, natural protocol for treating illnesses, including cancer, arthritis, and prostate problems

Dr. Ward Bond, owner
P.O. Box 6748
Kingwood, TX 77325
www.drwardbond.com

Optimal Natural Health
health products for women; ellagic acid (a strong antifungal)

Leilani Tejada, owner
11661 Preston Road, Suite 140
Dallas, TX 75230
www.blisscream.com
1.888.641.2547

80   QR

Books

Information about the health value of the colors in food

Joseph, J.A. Nadeau, D.A. Underwood, A. The color code; a revolutionary eating plan for optimum health. 2002. Hyperion, NY. ISBN 0-7868-6721-3

Information about dehydrating

The Dry Store
Mary T. Bell, proprietor
Route # 2 Box 156A
Lanesboro, MN
www.drystore.com
1.507.467.2928

Bell, Mary. Mary Bell's complete dehydrator cookbook. 1994. William Morrow and Company, NY. ISBN 0-688-13024-0

Information about fats and oils

Enig, M. E., Ph.D. Know your fats: the complete primer for understanding the nutrition of fats, oils, and cholesterol. 2000. Bethesda Press. Silver Spring, MD. ISBN 0-9678126-0-7

Basic information underlying this approach

MediaTrition
1.972.772.0990

Kaufmann, Doug A. The fungus link. 2000. MediaTrition. Rockwall, TX. ISBN 0-9703418-0-6

Kaufmann, Doug A. The germ that causes cancer. 2002. MediaTrition. Rockwall, TX. ISBN 0-9703418-1-4.

80 ଔ

Catalogues and Suppliers

The Baker's Catalogue

citrus oils, dried orange peel, dried onions, dried red and green peppers, unsweetened coconut, and other dried herbs and spices as well as kitchen utensils, cookware, and storage containers

> The Baker's Catalogue
> P.O. Box 876
> Norwich, VT 05055-0876
> www.kingarthurflour.com
> 1.800.827.6836
> fax: 1.800.343.3002

Brownwood Acres

unsweetened cherry, blueberry, and pomegranate juice concentrates, as well as unsweetened dried cherries, blueberries, and strawberries

> Brownwood Acres
> P.O. Box 486
> Eastport, MI. 49627
> www.brownwoodacres.com
> 1.877.591.3101

Morningside Buying Club

bulk tapioca flour, organic herbs/seeds, unsweetened fruit concentrates, organic yogurts, unsweetened coconut

> Morningside Natural Foods
> 215 Morningside Lane
> Liberty, TN 37095
> 1.615.563.2353
> www.morningsidefarm.com

North American Herb & Spice Co.

oil of oregano, oil of lavender, and other anti-fungal products

North American herb & Spice Co.
P. O. Box 4885
Buffalo Grove, IL 60089
1.800.243.5242

NOW Foods

organic, non-GMO food products, tea tree oil, lavender oil, essential oils, vitamins, minerals, herbs, flours, seeds, a number of different stevia products, as well as books, health tips, and natural pharmaceuticals.

NOW Foods
www.nowfoods.com

Penzeys Spices

Offer a wide variety of herbs, spices, flavorings, and extracts including specialty spices.

Penzeys Spices
www.penzeys.com
1.800.741.7787

restaurant supply store

An unusual place to find kitchenware, storage containers, and a variety of kitchen tools for less money than you would pay elsewhere. See listing in telephone books for larger cities.

I bought a slicer/grater that is one of my favorite tools. It makes quick work of slicing or grating larger quantities of onions, leeks, bell peppers, carrots, asparagus, cucumbers, etc., either to dehydrate, freeze, or have a ready supply of raw vegetables on hand for quick preparation of breakfast eggs or other vegetable dishes. With a ready supply of raw vegetables, I am encouraged to incorporate more of them into my diet.   *Beverly*

Seagate

olive leaf extracts, grape seed extract, beta glucans, and organic carrot powder

Seagate Products
9484 Chesapeake Dr. Suite 802
San Diego, CA 92123
1.888.505.GATE (4283)
www.SeagateProducts.com

Tropical Traditions

organic, virgin coconut oil ~ unrefined and cold-pressed

Tropical Traditions
823 South Main Street
West Bend, WI 53095
1.866.311.2626
www.tropicaltraditions.com

The Vitamin Shoppe

Nutribiotic® Grapefruit Seed Extract (*GSE*®) products, North American Herb & Spice Co. products (oil of oregano, oil of lavender)

The Vitamin Shoppe
www.vitaminshoppe.com
1.800.223.1216

- *Tips* -

arrowroot
> ~ Use less arrowroot to thicken liquid than you would use wheat flour.
>
> ~ Use 1 tablespoon to thicken 1 cup of liquid.

broccoli
> ~ One cup has 120 mg if vitamin C, more than the RDA for men or women.[5]

chips
> ~ Corn chips, potato chips, etc., whether baked or fried, contain acrylamide, a chemical used to make plastic. This chemical forms from the oils used during frying and baking at high temperatures. Laboratory rats fed acrylamide had increased rates of cancer, nerve damage, and infertility.
>
> ~ French fries have 200 times the amount of acrylamide than is allowed in normal drinking water.[6]

flaxseed
> ~ Ground flaxseed will last 90 days refrigerated or in the freezer.
>
> ~ Whole flaxseed will last 1 year at room temperature, refrigeration not needed.
>
> ~ Flax oil lasts 30 days, refrigerated. It is more susceptible to oxidation.

5. Engstrom, Martha, ed. Grandma's farm country cookbook. 1996. Voyageur Press. Stillwater, MN.

6. www.mercola.com   December 2003.

fresh herbs

~ Store in a jar covered with warmed vinegar. Will keep at room temperature for several years.[7]

~ Save time and money by purchasing herbs in bulk. Chop them, then divide into small amounts in labeled bags and freeze. They are ready for use when you need them without languishing in the vegetable drawer of the refrigerator.

honey

~ Measure honey with as little waste as possible:
- Warm and dry the measuring device.
- Spray the cup or spoon with non-stick spray or coat with vegetable oil

lemon

~ A bowl of fresh lemons will add fragrance and color to a room for days.

~ Add a slice of lemon to a glass of water. It has visual appeal and makes the water taste and smell better.

~ To reduce sodium, try squeezing a wedge of fresh lemon on salads, steamed vegetables, soups, or stews. You will be less likely to miss the salt.

~ Roll a room temperature lemon on the counter a few times to maximize the amount of juice extracted.

~ Add the grated zest of a fresh lemon to recipes. Zest adds intensity to dessert recipes.

mustard

~ Can be mild, nippy, or hot. The heat is regulated by how long the freshly-prepared mustard mixture stays at room temperature before being refrigerated.[8]
(see "Mustard" in Condiments and Dressings.)

~ 1 tsp dry mustard = 1 tbsp prepared mustard

--- --- --- --- --- --- --- --- --- ---

7. Tightwad living's vinegar book. PO Box 629, Burgin, KY. 40310-0629
8. Penzeys Spices. www.penzeys.com January 2004.

oils / fats

~ There is a long-standing, growing body of evidence that saturated fats (animal and tropical oils) from organic, pasteur-fed/free range sources are a better choice for heat-related cooking because vegetable oils form trans fatty acids and will oxidize when heated.

Our recommendation is to locate organic, unrefined tropical oils (coconut or palm) from sources that practice acceptable manufacturing processes for use in all recipes that require oil heated to high temperatures.

ଔ   ଓ

- *Tools* -

There are excellent, reliable tools on the market suitable for these suggested food preparations. Some described are on the upper end of possibilities, though these are not the only ones on the market. Writing this book gave me the impetus to get them, but the households of my three children have not included all of them in their budgets. Like these households, choose tools that fit your space and budget.

The "tooling" grandmother,   *Beverly*

apple-peeler-corer-slicer

This adapted screw mechanism winds the apple off the core in a continuous thin sliced piece. This tool can prepare raw apple snacks in a jiffy. The apple "slinky" is appealing to children and is a form to inspire a cook's decorative impulses.

Kali apple peeler: $299.95
www.homesteadharvest.com

Williams-Sonoma $28.00
www.williams-sonoma.com

immersion blender

A handy tool, quick and easy to use, easy to clean. Saves getting out the bigger blender. It does not have the raw power of a Vitamix,™ but I love to use it to purée vegetables for soup or to whip cream. My son makes oat flour from oatmeal with his.

Thunder Stick Pro $39.95 + s/h
Thane International Inc.
La Quinta, CA. 92253
1.800.982.4405
www.thane.com

mandoline

Useful as a slicing tool. Take care! I just *touched* the blade to see if it WAS a blade and got a nasty cut on my finger. It comes with a food pusher…with good reason. The one from Chef's is a quality one, but there are versions which are less expensive.

models up to $169.00 at www.chefscatalogue.com

Hofritz - $69.99 at www.amazon.com

a $99.99 model at www.creativecookware.com

Vitamix™

A blender, chopper, mixer, food processor, meat grinder, raw soup maker, etc. A very strong blender that can stand up to hard use. This appliance can do the work of several appliances. It makes unsurpassed smoothies and soups. The available grinder blade can grind flour. I have seen this appliance in a restaurant supply store.

Vita-Mix Corporation
Household Division
8615 Usher Rd.
Cleveland, OH, 44138
FAX 440.235.3726
www.household@vitamix.com

80 C8

Terms & Glossary

aflatoxin B1 - (*Aflatoxin bisfurano*) - compounds produced primarily by the molds *Aspergillus flavus* and *Aspergillus perisiticus*; a toxic compound, the most potent known carcinogen[1]

almond flour - ground from nut meats after oils are removed; give baked goods a finer texture; has 6g essential carbohydrates in one-half cup compared to 42g carbohydrates in unbleached wheat flour; can substitute almond meal

almond meal - ground from whole nuts; grittier and oiler than the flour; gives baked goods a moister, coarser texture

antibiotic - compound of high molecular weight produced by microbes; has specific toxic effects on other microbes sensitive to it[2]

apple cider vinegar - *see* vinegar

arrowroot - thickener and substitute for wheat flour; usage requires about one-half the amount required by wheat flour. Generally available where health foods are sold.

bacon - use fresh organic bacon; avoid preservatives (especially nitrates and nitrates) and curing which uses sugars

black olives - use those packed in water - they are not fermented

----

1. Cheek, P. R. Natural toxicants in feeds, forages and poisonous plants. 1998. Interstate Publishers Inc. Danville, IL.
2. Moore-Landecker, E. Fundamentals of fungi. 1996. Prentice-Hall. Upper Saddle River, NJ.

Bragg's Liquid Aminos - all-purpose seasoning from non-GMO soy protein; is not fermented. A good substitute for soy sauce.

broth - *see Processes*

boiled dressing - a mayonnaise substitute; *see Dressings*

butter - use organic to avoid antibiotics and hormones
    clarified butter or ghee - *see Processes*; does not easily burn at medium to high heat like regular butter
    unsalted butter - store in the freezer

capers - a flower bud; use capers *not* in vinegar (i.e., *not* pickled)

carbohydrate - one of three major food constituents; fats and proteins are the other two

carotene - red or orange compound found in carrots, sweet potatoes, milk fat, egg yolk, and leafy vegetables; changes to vitamin A in the body. A body that cannot digest carotene may become lacking in vitamin A.[3]

celeriac - autumn/early winter vegetable; substitute for potatoes; a root crop and member of the parsley family with a celery-like taste whose root bulb grows to four inches in diameter or more. Usually available at health food markets or higher-end grocery stores.

coconut oil - a tropical oil used for high heat cooking processes and in baking; useful for persons with compromised immune sysytems; does not promote chemical carcinogenesis. Coconut oil also has antimicrobial properties, aids in the health of the immune system, and protects against harmful microorganisms in the digestive tract.[4,5]

---

3. Mosby's Medical Encyclopedia. 1997. The Learning Company Inc.
4. Enig, M. Health and nutrituional benefits from coconut oil: an important functional food for the 21st century. Presented at the AVOC Lauric Oils Symposium. Apr 1996. Ho Chi Min City, Vietnam.
5. Enig, M., Fallon S. The Skinny on Fats. The Weston A. Price Foundation. www.westonaprice.org   12/28/03

conidium - fungal spore released inside a living organism; capable of reproducing by cloning (wall-deficient, non-sexual)[6]

cream cheese - use only if cream is the only ingredient; look for organic to avoid antibiotics and hormones

cream, heavy - very low carbohydrate count; *see Diet* for further information

cream, sour - use only if cream is the only ingredient; try to find organic to avoid antibiotics and hormones

cream, whipping - very low carbohydrate count; *see* cream, heavy

Dutch oven - large, heavy, metal pot with a tight-fitting lid

egg - best from range-free chickens; *see Diet*

fats/oils - saturated fats (coconut, palm, beef tallow, lard, butter) are highly stable and do not normally go rancid even when heated for cooking purposes; unsaturated and polyunsaturated fats (liquid vegetable oils) are not stable and create trans fatty acids when they are heated

feta cheese - made from sheep or goat's milk[7]

flax meal/seed - the richest plant source of omega-3; also rich source of lignans and fiber. Flax meal serves as good substitute for butter or oils in muffin and bread recipes; use a 3 to 1 ratio of flax meal to oil.

fritatta - egg dish or omelet

— — — — — — — — — —

6. Moore-Landecker, E. Fundamentals of fungi. 1990. Prentice-Hall. Englewood Cliffs, NJ.

7. Margon, S., eds. University of California, Berkeley. The wellness encyclopaedia of food and nutrition. How to buy, store, and prepare every variety of fresh food. 1992. Rebus. NY.

glucose - most important carbohydrate in body metabolism;[8] *see* metabolism

gluten - substance in wheat flour that makes the cooked recipe light in texture; has 6g carbohydrates in one-quarter cup[9]

GSE® - Grapefruit Seed Extract; *see Sources* and *Processes*

hazelnuts - smaller American relative of the European filbert; good source of folacin, calcium, iron, and magnesium

honey - use organic, raw unpasteurized honey when possible; contains the antifungal malic acid

ham/pork - find organic sources; *see* bacon

immune system - bodily system that identifies foreign substances and prevents them from harming the body[2]

Italian sausage - make sure ingredients list includes only allowed foods; should not include nitrites, nitrates, or sugars in its processing

low carbohydrate - good for this diet but not the only criterion for inclusion in the diet; *see Diet*

mélange - a mixture

mycotoxin - substances produced by mold growing in food or animal feed; causes illness or death when ingested by humans or animals[5]

nutraceutical - foods that act as medicines

non-stick spray - avoid canola oil; use an olive oil spray instead

_____

8. Thomas, C. L., et. al., eds. Tabors' Cyclopedic Medical Dictionary. 1997. F A Davis Co. Philadelphia, PA.
9. Turner, L. Going against the grain. 6(10). 38-41. October 2003. Great Life.

olive oil - extra-virgin oil is the first pressing and has been processed without heat or chemicals; "light" refers to taste as well as texture and color

orange oil - sold as a flavoring; high percentage of pure orange oil is d-limonene, an anticancerous substance. Applied topically, it even helps ameliorate the itch of an insect bite.

phytochemical - recently created term that emphasizes the plant source of most plant-derived protective, disease-preventing compounds; true nutritional role for phytochemicals is becoming more probable every day as research uncovers more of their remarkable benefits. In fact, the term phytonutrient better describes the compounds' "quasi-nutrient" status. Someday, phytochemicals may indeed be classified as essential nutrients.[9]

produce washing - *see Processes*

psyllium - a tiny seed; when ground is a good source of fiber to aid with bowel regularity

seeds - *see Processes*

soup - *see Processes*

soy - a legume; often a GMO: a genetically modified organism; not recommended on this diet because it is difficult for the ordinary cook to determine if the soy bean or product is a GMO

steroid - term applied to any one of a large group of substances chemically related to sterols[2]

stevia - from the leaves of the shrub *Stevia rebaudiana*; 200 to 300 times sweeter than sugar[10]

_____

10. DePuydt, R. Baking with stevia. Recipes for the sweet leaf. 1997. Sun Coast Enterprises. USA.

stick blender - *see Products*

stock - *see Processes*

tapioca flour - *see Processes*

thickener - *see Processes*

unsandwich - sandwiches plated without bread

vegetable oils - many besides olive oil, such as sesame, grape seed, etc.; nut and seed oils are prone to spoilage, so store in the refrigerator. Bring to room temperature before using. Cloudiness from refrigeration will disappear when it returns to room temperature.

vinaigrette - sauce made of vinegar, salt, pepper, and herbs

vinegar - use organic, unpasteurized apple cider vinegar: is not fermented and contains the antifungal malic acid

virus - striking similarity between the medical dictionary definition of virus and Dr. M. White's definition of the fungal spore that causes cancer

water - filtered is best

yogurt - avoid yogurt with sugar or artificial sweetener as ingredient; best if organic, plain yogurt

yucca - source of vitamin C, easily-absorbed iron, and magnesium; tapioca, manioc, casava, and yucca are all the same plant. More yucca is grown in the world than potatoes.

zest - colorful part of citrus rind; obtained by grating. Freeze in order to have on hand to use in cooking.

Index

Notes